ACROSS *THE* SPECTRUM

Mothers of Autistic Children Speak!

Anne Tucker Roberts

Anne Tucker Roberts

OMNI PUBLISHING CO.

2021

Published by
Omni Publishing Co.
www.omni-pub.com
October 2021

Library of Congress cataloging-in-publication data
Roberts, Anne Tucker
Across the Spectrum: Mothers of Autistic Children Speak!
ISBN: 978-1-928758-03-7

Printed in the United States of America

Cover Design: DerbyCreative.com

Group Photo, Photographic Design and Layout: David Heath, CPP

With such appreciation for all my students –
And the lessons they imparted.

This book is in memory of my father,
William Duane Tucker, Jr.,
Who introduced me to curiosity,
And the ingredients to make a meaningful life.

It is dedicated to
My husband, John, for his steady presence
And to
My brother, Carlton,
Whose resilience and lightheartedness
Inspires.

Table of Contents

Introduction

by Judith Scott, MD

As a physician and mother of a young man with autism, I thought I knew it all. But what I discovered while reading *Across the Spectrum* is that just because I have *lived* it doesn't mean that I *know* it.

Herein lie tales of uncertainty and perseverance, heartbreak and empowerment, setbacks and stunning success. *Across the Spectrum* is essential reading for anyone who wants to understand autism better. You will discover that autism is a spectrum of abilities and disabilities and that standardized assessments notoriously underestimate potential. These stories reveal many of the reasons behind the behaviors and idiosyncrasies of people on the spectrum and offer key considerations for promoting communication and progress.

Across the Spectrum looks at six families over 40 years, from the early 1970s to the 21st century. We meet parents who raised their child without knowing the word "autism," to those caught in the uncertainties of labels forging ahead to blaze trails of their own, to younger parents implementing modern-day therapies developed through the intervening years.

 Extensive research into Autism Spectrum Disorder over the last three decades has provided remarkable advances. There are better tools for detection and intervention, and community and professional resources are more available than ever before. However, there is a LONG way to go toward fully understanding one of today's most confounding medical mysteries. One certainty, however, endures: parents will always be the front line, bearing the heaviest burden in providing for these children. This book brings to life the ways in which siblings, aunts, uncles, grandparents, teachers, and friends can be essential allies in forging a path through the challenges of life with autism.

A professor of Developmental Pediatrics once described entering a classroom of children with autism in this way: "In the first five minutes you notice how similar they are. After five minutes, you notice just how different each one is." The myriad traits and vast array of truly remarkable skills described in these stories epitomize this statement and make for fascinating reading.

Across the Spectrum brims with practical information and key truths for success in a life with autism. More importantly, it offers solidarity and inspiration for caretakers and brings us one step further toward a world where "different" is not just OK, but beautiful and wondrous.

Dr. Judith Scott is a graduate of Princeton University and The Geisel School of Medicine at Dartmouth. She has been board-certified in Internal Medicine for 26+ years. She is raising a child with autism and has helped raise funds for The New England Center for Children, a school for children with Autism Spectrum Disorder in Southborough, MA.

Millie and Bobby

Classic Autism ?

1978

Bobby was different from my other children. He was my fourth, born in February 1978. It was when Bobby turned two that I noticed delays. Each of his siblings reached their developmental milestones on schedule but not Bobby. He did not walk until he was seventeen months and was not potty trained until the age of four.

Those lags were problematic, but he had other unusual traits for his age. As a toddler, part of his daily routine was to climb up onto the couch with a telephone book. There he would study the pages quietly for hours. By the age of two, he loved reading the numbers lit up on digital clocks, and soon was rattling off digits as if they were his private language. Yet there were no words; he spoke only numbers. We speculated but thought maybe he was just unusually gifted!

There were other peculiarities. Bobby rarely made eye contact and always had a distant, blank stare. He also showed no curiosity for the world around him, and in our family of five, he was a loner, preferring to play by himself. Strange, too, was his rigid adherence to routine. When he left his bedroom each morning, he carried his bucket of blocks, Lincoln Logs, and Matchbook cars. He plopped himself down and began constructing a maze. The maze was so grand that it took over our entire living room. He took a break for lunch but then went right back to it. At nap time each day, he dismantled it completely. Then out he marched again, after his nap, ready to start all over again. This routine went on every day for years.

When the last block was in place, he would come into the kitchen, open the silverware drawer and take out all the teaspoons. With great purpose, he would tuck them into his maze. Then he would place his small plastic Texaco sign in its spot. Baffling – until one day, we figured it out. Bobby was replicating the main street in Rockland, complete with McDonald's, the train tracks, and, of course, the Texaco gas station. So, while Bobby did not convey curiosity about the world around him, he *was* observant!

He was also in charge. Bobby was so engrossed in this project that nobody could bother him, not at all. If by chance you did disturb him, a tantrum ensued. His silence was deafening, his concentration extraordinary.

In time, that fixation finally disappeared, but new ones always surfaced. One of the most frustrating fetishes Bobby developed was tearing labels out of his clothes – all his clothes – from shirts to pants to jackets and even coats. Unfortunately, when the label came off, so did all the thread around it, which left gaping holes. I might not have discovered this had Bobby's obsession not extended to *my* clothing and, I noticed, to my husband Jimmy's.

As if the labels weren't enough, Bobby soon began removing shirt pockets and the thread along the bottom of his shirts. Who knew that tongues in sneakers were held together by a thread? They, too, disappeared! Bobby's biggest "de-threading" project was yanking out every short and long strand from the quilt on his bed. His fluffy comforter soon became a thin, limp throw. For years, Bobby was consumed with this costly craze despite trying everything to get him to break the habit. Eventually, he "de-threaded" things less and less until, thankfully, it seemed to have run its course.

4

A relief! That is until his next fixation emerged. At age ten, Bobby latched on to watching "World Wrestling Entertainment" (WWE). When these two-hour matches ended, he would immediately round up his wrestling figures and start playing. But this was not ordinary play. His face turned beat red and sweat dripped freely. Once again, nobody could disrupt him. I worried as I watched him retreat into his world. His brother, Adam, finally figured it out. Bobby was reenacting the match they had just watched. "He's flipping over the same wrestlers and celebrating the guys who won."

observe

While I was troubled by Bobby's unusual habits like maze building and his preoccupation with ripping out threads, I had a far more profound concern – his temper. For years, the only way to get him away from his maze and out of the house was to sneak up behind and grab him, leading to a burst of bone-chilling hysterics. I had to wrestle him into his jacket and drag him out screaming.

Bobby suffered these fits often, sometimes for reasons unknown. At those times, I tried cradling him and speaking gently; most times, however, I'd have to let him carry on and wear himself out. Often, he ended up climbing onto the couch and falling fast asleep.

By chance, I found a fix – music, any music. I would turn the stereo on when Bobby was young and begin my housework. Peering in to make sure he was okay, I found that he had made his way up onto the couch and was sitting trance-like. Since music worked in peaceful times, I decided to try it when he went into a fit. It worked – sometimes.

Bobby's peculiarities were complicated, his stormy rants were troubling, but his lack of language was such a barrier. It frustrated him and distressed us. What speech he did have – numbers and gibberish – made no sense. He gained a few words and soon began repeating what he heard others say. We would frequent my mother's pool in the nice weather where, undoubtedly, she would be hollering at my irritating younger brother. Once home and in his room, we heard Bobby call out, "Patrick, stop that. Patrick, go to time out." I learned that there is a name for this quirkiness – *Echolalia*.

As problems mounted, I knew something was wrong but did not know what. Bobby's pediatrician would only say, "All children are different. These are just delays; there is probably nothing to fret about. He'll come along."

I waited.

One day, I mentioned my concerns to my incredibly wise mother, who suggested I call the school department to assess him. The town's special education director advised a "core evaluation" for Bobby and steered us to the Early Childhood Center at the North River Collaborative. (The North River Collaborative, NRC, is a multi-purpose, educational organization formed in 1976 to serve as an extension of nine school districts in neighboring towns.) The memory of that day, thirty-seven years ago, is as vivid now as it was then. All Bobby did during the screening was run around the room, flap his hands, and scream, "Cut it out, cut it out!" He did not respond to people, sit in a chair, or cooperate with anyone's requests. I was mortified. What's more, I was sure they would never let this four-year-old come near their classroom. He was too much trouble.

The program's director let Bobby ride a Big Wheel back and forth and up and down a long corridor. She and I sat on the steps, me nearly in tears, her trying to console me. "We can help," she said kindly and proposed that Bobby come for a second session, accompanied by his Dad. A couple of weeks later, Jimmy had his turn. Wouldn't you know there were no significant behavioral issues?

During this second evaluation, Bobby cooperated, but he could not do many of the tasks. Placement did not appear promising. To my delight, however, he was accepted. A few weeks later, *routine*

Bobby began in the NRC's Early Childhood Center (ECC) and remained there until he was seven. They had a well-defined routine which helped him settle in better than we expected.

At seven, Bobby transitioned to a program at our local middle school. There were other classmates with special needs in the room but none like Bobby. He learned ten sight words a day and soon talking in numbers disappeared, and short sentences like "I want milk" began. However, it took three full years for Bobby to become fluent. (So much for another milestone he missed.)

Excited by how quickly Bobby was catching on, his aide put a piece of drawing paper in front of him one day, "Here you go. Make *Bobby*." Rather than create a picture of himself, he simply wrote: B O B B Y. Little did we know that he could even spell his name. I saved that picture for a long time.

While he started to improve in reading, writing and talking, Bobby still had behavior issues. He had a one-on-one aide because he had the propensity to bolt. His escapes were abrupt, spontaneous, and always scary, leaving the aide to chase after him. Strangely enough, once caught and returned to the classroom, he was fine. Stranger still was that nobody could figure out what prompted them; one minute, he appeared calm and attentive; the next, he was gone. He never explained why but would sheepishly say, "Sorry."

Bobby had a lot of anxiety and still does today. We never knew where it originated. Medication was not suggested for his temper tantrums when he was young, but recommended when the tantrums continued into middle school.

Having a fit as a toddler, I could rock him on my lap to soothe him. Later, when they occurred, he would rest his head on my shoulder, awaiting my caress. The tumultuous day became as peaceful as a lullaby. But one day, without warning, all fondling ended. Nobody, not even me, can even touch him anymore, not at all, not even a little. It continues to this day, thirty years later. He will hug me if my arms are at my side, but I cannot hug him back. I have come close to begging.

Somebody told me that touching hurts certain people with autism. "It feels like a sunburn," they explained. But why? And why so suddenly did this come about? I don't know. I used to hold his hand all the time, and he held mine. I miss those days.

Being touched, however, is inescapable. Sometimes it's predictable, other times not. My husband takes him to the same barbershop every month. When Bobby walks in, the barber sings out, "Hey Buddy! How are you?" All a fluster, Bobby makes a beeline to the men's room. Once inside, he starts jabbering – making chirping and grunting noises – trying to release the anxiety swelling inside. Jimmy, too, shudders as he braces for what they both know comes next. When the bathroom door opens and Bobby reappears, the barber will dash towards him and slap him on the shoulder with exuberance. Bobby usually tolerates it. Then Jimmy can exhale.

Bobby knows that all doctors have to touch him. I prepare him for his physical; his father always accompanies him. Jimmy returned once with a funny story. The physician explained that he was going to check Bobby's reflexes. He took out the small hammer and rapped Bobby's knee with it. Bobby instinctively struck back, whacking the poor guy on the shoulder. The doctor never made a big deal of it and even learned to expect it. Luckily for everyone, Bobby eventually lost that impulse.

Bobby's knee-jerk reaction was never meant to hurt anyone, but suddenly again, around the age of five or six, that too changed, and a frightening new streak emerged. Bobby became aggressive. I called our DDS service coordinator for help. (DDS is the state-run Department of Developmental Services.) She urged us to take him into Boston's Children's Hospital. We did not hesitate. After a full day's evaluation, they could only tell us, "He has autistic tendencies." (Later, we learned that the policy at Children's Hospital was to withhold labels. A label, they thought, would further alienate children in school and lower the expectations of professionals.)

We did get a label, but it was four years later when Bobby was ten. We were at our wits end. We took Bobby to see a psychiatrist at Harvard Vanguard Medical Associates and pleaded for help. I told the doctor about Children's Hospital's "tendencies for autism" assessment and described his behaviors in detail. Bobby stood behind me, flailing various hand gestures above my head. Finally, so distracted, the doctor declared, "You're right, he is a classic case." (Flailing is what is referred to as "hand flapping." It is also known as "stimming." Behaviors such as flapping, rocking, and pacing are often characterized by rigid, repetitive movements or vocal sounds. Bobby had exhibited these since he was a toddler.)

After that session, Bobby began seeing a therapist who identified him as having a mild intellectual disability. Both these diagnoses made him eligible for a variety of state services, one of which was a more appropriate special ed program at St. Coletta's Day School, a private school in Braintree. He immediately transitioned there and remained until graduating at age twenty-two.

Most children are excited to go to school on a bus. Bobby needed prepping – straight talk with no wiggle room, "You're going to a new school." Bobby began to work himself into a lather pouring out his cavalcade of questions. Finally, he seemed ready, but we still faced daily battles to get him on the bus. Once school became routine, the fighting ceased.

St. Coletta's encountered far fewer behavioral incidents than his previous public school. However, there were times when Bobby became obstinate and flat-out refused to do things. He also came into that pubescent age of thinking he could outsmart people. Jimmy and I were frequently called in, often to talk with Kay Toma, an excellent teacher who loved Bobby. She was eventually worn down trying to manage his outbursts. Administrators moved him to a class with a more demanding teacher, and those conning behaviors evaporated.

As students age at St. Coletta's, they move to an onsite job training program formerly called a "workshop." Bobby became a noteworthy assembly worker with exceptionally fine motor skills. He could sit in this noisy environment, work for hours, and complete the tasks correctly, rendering him a small paycheck. "He'll be a taxpayer soon!" they smiled.

With his newfound fortune, he relished the opportunity to go out to eat. Bliss for Bobby comes in the form of burgers, fries, and a bottle of water. He was now at the age when he wanted to order for himself. With pen in hand, the waitress asked, "So, how do you want your burger?" As if on cue, Bobby responded, "Cooked."

Even as Bobby ages, he is happiest following a strict schedule. His mornings operate like clockwork, his afternoons the same. If dinner is ready ten minutes earlier than 6:00, Bobby refuses to come to the table until the minute hand strikes twelve. The hours after dinner are also dictated by the clock. Weekends run a little differently because he likes to sleep in, but only until nine. Saturdays, "Entertainment Day," is spent with his Dad. Sundays are his "Day of Rest."

For forty-one years, we have done everything we could to make sure Bobby's life runs smoothly – no delays, postponements, interruptions, or surprises. But when things have not gone as planned, he has had dramatic meltdowns. These have gone on for decades. He will flare up, given anything spontaneous. Unexpected visitors, even if they are his siblings, will unnerve him. Disasters are averted if I can prepare him.

"So and so is coming tomorrow," I explain.

"Well, why is he coming?" Bobby asks. "Is anyone else coming? What time is he coming? How long is he going to be here?"

When his brothers and sisters were younger, I explained that

10

Bobby was different and would require more patience. For the most part, they simply left him alone and accepted him the way he is – differences and all. There were no judgments or even discussions about his peculiarities. Each knows he loves them despite his seeming indifference to them.

The four of them have always watched over him. Once my mother unknowingly handed Bobby a fork. They piped up simultaneously, "Oh no, Bobby does not like forks; he wants a spoon." One added, "That's just Bobby." Bobby insists on a spoon for everything. I tried to change that, but he flew into a tantrum every time.

My children love him as a brother and my husband, Jimmy, is crazy about him. Bobby considers his father "second fiddle" to me, despite all Jimmy does for him. Jimmy not only brings Bobby to every medical appointment and his monthly haircut, but for forty-one years he has also taken him out to dinner and the movies every Saturday. And yes, to avoid touching elbows, he remembers to leave an empty seat between them.

On Thursday nights, from the time Bobby was three, Jimmy has also taken him grocery shopping, but only if it is on Thursday. If the day has to change, for some reason, Bobby refuses to go. (We discovered along the way that Bobby had become a bit of a kleptomaniac, shoplifting Oreo cookies and giant Hershey bars. Telling him that police would arrest him stopped that in its tracks.)

For the last ten years, Jimmy also takes him to Old Orchard Beach in Maine for a much-anticipated summer vacation. It's just the two of them, and it is "All About Bobby." They do not skip any of his favorite things: the beach, arcade, waterslides, bowling, movies, and of course, his favorite restaurants, including mandatory stops at Dairy Queen.

Initially, the three of us went for a week every summer. We treasured the thought of our beautiful unit right on the beach. However, Bobby did not make it a very relaxing time. The clock dictated every minute. It became more nerve-wracking when family members came for a day or two. Despite our attempts to keep Bobby happy, there were far too many incidents of him acting out (hitting, screaming, yelling, etc.)

It was our only vacation week. I hate to say that Bobby ruined it because I realize it was not his fault, but being on edge the entire trip meant we came home exhausted. Hearing this, my sister offered to take Bobby for that week. Bobby loves his "Auntie Ree and Uncle Dave," and their dog, Sadie, but the actual lure is their beautiful in-ground pool. And us? We love being on the beach in Maine by ourselves.

We had pangs of guilt not taking him with us and did not have the heart to tell him why. So, we set the father-son Maine trip in motion, and when it came time for *our* vacation, we told him that we were going to Florida. Flying is out for Bobby. Everyone wins despite this small white lie.

Along with loving Oreos, Hershey bars, and trips to Old Orchard Beach, Bobby also loves his DVDs. He owns hundreds (Superman, Batman, Lassie, etc.) and watches them again and again. He also replays DVD movies he enjoyed in theaters and those from his siblings' weddings.

Bobby likes going to the movies, but he has never been overly excited by television. If he is in the living room, he will have the TV on a weather or music channel. He is captivated by all weather conditions but gets panicky hearing storm predictions – any storm, even rain. I try to downplay the report saying, "It's no big deal; the sun will come out tomorrow."

As a youngster, there were two programs he would never miss: "The Dukes of Hazard" and "The Price Is Right." One day, he casually asked me, "Why does Bob Barker have white hair today?" I looked and thought it odd that Mr. Barker's hair turned white overnight. Then I remembered other times Bobby was that observant. He notices everything about *me*, making comments like

"I love you in that pink shirt." Maybe that is to be expected. But when he was much younger, we would often travel to visit my mother. On the way, he pointed to the sky once and asked, "How come they put wires there?" I had no clue what he meant until it dawned on me that he had been keeping track of new lines going up for cable TV. His keen memory and visual acuity are still uncanny. Once, I had to drive him to his adult day program. Being unsure of the directions, I asked him to tell me when to turn. Well, that was a mistake! He told me when to go right and left, but I seemed to be making these turns a little too often. He got me there all right, following the route his van took every day.

Bobby also has a rare intuition. He senses if I seem the least bit upset about something. "What's wrong?" he'll ask. "Is there something I should know?" I assure him that it has nothing to do with him, but he will still approach me, saying, "I want to give you a hug; I want you to be happy." I remember as a young boy; he would come face to face with me, break into a pronounced smile and say, "Put on a happy face like this." He is funny even though he might not know he is funny.

On the rare occasion that Jimmy and I get into a disagreement, Bobby will call out, "What's all the commotion about? I hope there's no divorce coming?" He does not like quarrels, not one little bit; they worry him.

Bobby's temperament and quirky behaviors do not interfere with his ability to love. It is clear to Jimmy and me, who are privileged to see that sweet and affectionate side of him. Unfortunately, others are not usually allowed in. But Derek is. "My pal Derek" is Bobby's best friend. He was often at our house since he was my daughter Julie's first boyfriend. Bobby took a liking to Derek and vice versa. As that connection grew, we asked Derek if he would like to take Bobby (then age fourteen) out for lunch and the movies on occasional Saturdays. Derek said yes, and Bobby lived for those days.

A few years later, Derek and Julie went their separate ways.

We did not say anything but wondered if Derek still wanted to take Bobby out. To our delight, Derek never skipped a beat – or a movie. Their outing has gone on for twenty years, even though Derek has had many changes in his life. He's married (Bobby was an usher at his wedding), moved twenty miles away, and has two boys of his own.

There are plenty of memorable stories watching Bobby grow up but – oh, those tantrums! Around the age of fourteen, Bobby became more aggressive and more violent. He was fully grown by then, and at 5'7", that anger was scary. His outbursts had always been rough, but these were on a whole different level. Every day something or someone would set him off; often, we had no idea what. For some unknown reason, Jimmy was the target, but that never stopped Bobby from hitting my other children or me. Some days this was nonstop. More than once, he would pound his fist on our glass-top coffee table and shatter it. He would cut his hand on other things too, but nothing stopped him. One day, my husband accidentally brushed up against him as he left the house. When Jimmy reached the back door, Bobby lunged in his direction smashing the door's window. It all became too frightening.

We reached out for help again and connected with a psychologist from South Shore Mental Health named Jan Harris. Hearing about the many traumatic incidents, she quickly created a strict behavior chart for Bobby. Jan explained, "You are going to give him a "**V**" (checkmark) and a happy face for good behavior or an "**X**" and a sad face for bad behavior." "Marks," she said, "have to be made every ten minutes, all day." We were willing to try anything.

I sat with Bobby at the dining room table and explained the process. His agitation began. He started kicking me under the table. Then he began repeating in a deep, breathy, nearly inaudible whisper, "F***You; F*** You!" I thought to myself, "This is not my child! We don't say that." Still, I could not lose my resolve.

It was slow going at first, but happy faces were now what we were living for. We encouraged good behavior by reviewing his chart throughout the day. However, his outbursts were still so frequent that Jan had to come weekly. Bobby hated seeing the sad faces and reading the negative notations, but ultimately, they were the catalyst for change. I soon caught him taking the charts to his room to read. Eventually, more good days piled up, and we could spread the ten-minute intervals out to every half hour, then to every hour. But that clipboard remained on our kitchen counter for thirty years!

While some of Bobby's challenging behaviors have softened, many still require our attention. Bobby does not like many people around, but it's inevitable with a pool in the backyard. Adults and little ones come all the time. Despite efforts to prepare him, he is never comfortable. If a group is on one side of the pool, Bobby is on the other. If they swim to his side, he hurries away. It's hard because the pool is his sanctuary. Things can escalate when he hears the inevitable screaming and high shrills from little girls. Sometimes he grabs them, pleading, "Shut up!" He has never hurt anyone, but we reached our tipping point, "If you cannot keep your hands off others, you cannot go in the pool!" The threat of banning him worked; he has not touched anyone since.

Bobby's poor social skills have to be my biggest frustration. After wincing too many times, I decided to outline every detail of any upcoming event whether it be a cookout or a party and review it with him ad nauseum. Bobby would have a barrage of questions for me each time.

Preplanning steadies him, but there are always surprises. At my daughter's wedding, Bobby was dancing up a storm just as he prefers – alone. My sister later told us that when she got up to dance with him, he hastily announced, "I'll be right back." "Off he went to the men's room," she laughed, "and never returned."

Other times were not so humorous. My large family throws a huge Christmas party every year. We have outgrown each other's homes, so we rent a hall. Bobby is always eager to know who will be there. But his idea of a perfect party is to sit off by himself where he can observe everyone. He doesn't want anyone chatting him up, and he surely doesn't want anyone touching him. Every year I emphasize, "If you are going to go, people will want to talk to you. You have to answer them, and you have to be polite." He squirms but says he understands.

My warning works, sometimes. If people overdo it and get on his nerves, anything can happen. One Christmas, he blatantly yelled at his grandparents, who had submerged him in conversation. That was it for me! I left him home the following year, explaining, "You didn't behave appropriately." With saucer eyes, he asked, "I'm going to miss the party?" He was stunned, but it worked.

The next year, noting the gala on the calendar, he asked, "Are you going to take me?"

"If you behave yourself. If you are not going to be nice, you might as well stay home."

"No, I'll be good," he promised.

Every Christmas since then, he has been okay. Like his behavior in the pool, we have no idea how he can suddenly turn a switch off and keep it off.

In February 2000, Bobby turned twenty-two, which meant his school life came to an end. Through DDS, he was placed in a workshop called GROW. It was housed in a building beside a plastic manufacturing company. Occasionally that company hired individuals from the workshop. Within months, they learned of Bobby's skill level and hired him. He was trained to bag and wrap washing machine hoses. Quickly his production rate soared, and he seemed happy, which was all that mattered. One day, however, I noticed large bruises on his shoulders. When asked, he told me that one of his co-workers punched him. It was confirmed. The other employee explained that Bobby was annoying him by trying to reach into his pockets. I did not believe that for a minute, he would never get that close to anyone.

Another time Bobby came home limping. He denied that anything had happened. I had him take off his socks only to find a swollen and badly bruised foot. The workshop reported that Bobby was loading boxes onto a truck, and a pallet landed on his foot. We dashed to the doctor who declared it broken.

We discovered early on that Bobby has an unusually high pain tolerance. At age four, he fell off the jungle gym playing with his four siblings. He didn't cry or act as though he was hurt, so Jimmy did not think too much about it. But lifting Bobby's arm to take off his shirt that night, Bobby's shriek could have shattered glass. Off to the hospital they flew, only to learn that Bobby broke an elbow and dislocated a shoulder. On top of such remorse, Jimmy had to witness the doctors snapping Bobby's shoulder back into place.

I questioned GROW as to what kind of supervision the plastic company provided and learned that there was little, if any. That was that. We quickly found another day program called "Road to Responsibility," where he remains today.

We count on supervisors wherever he goes. Our greatest worry is that people will recognize Bobby's naivety and take advantage of his innocence. We constantly probe, but a simple question such as, "What did you do today?" is too broad, eliciting only "Nothing" or "I don't know." We would be left in the dark without his case manager.

As content and well-liked as he is at Road to Responsibility, Bobby still needs a watchful eye and tactful cajoling. He can be lazy and inflexible. He works hard at what he likes but doggedly refuses to do other things. Bobby will not work in the warehouse area; he refuses all collating jobs and will not go on any community outings. He doesn't argue the point. Instead, he calmly states, "No, thank you." "Bobby," I ask, "Why did you refuse to work?"

"I needed to relax myself," he replies. Or "I wasn't in the

mood." For the most part, thankfully, he is in the mood, and they love that he is a high producer.

Up until 2019, our life has been Bobby. After forty-one years of living with him, I suspect I could teach a class on autism. But the scope of autism is too broad – behaviors too unique. Each week Bobby presents surprises. For example, we found out the hard way the necessity for setting "parental controls" on anything electronic.

We have known that Bobby loves to play games and watch (free) videos on his Kindle Fire, but one afternoon, I learned just how clever he is. While checking my emails, I was startled to notice new ones, lots of them, all from Amazon thanking me for my video purchases. Looking closely, a light dawned. Batman? The Incredible Hulk series? These weren't for Jimmy! Bobby had ordered a total of one hundred and forty-four videos at $1.99 to $2.99 each.

I quickly called Amazon and explained what happened. Luckily, the customer service representative was sympathetic and agreed to credit my account. The only problem was that I had to stay on the phone while he reversed each charge. That gave me plenty of time to think. An hour went by. The representative finally came back on and told me to go back in and make sure all refunds were listed. I had to adjust my glasses – right in front of me were thirty to forty *new* emails from Amazon thanking me again for *my purchase*. Yes, Bobby had been up in his room ordering more videos! Embarrassed and exasperated, I explained my problem. Thankfully, he laughed. After another hour, we seemed squared away. My statement for that month arrived in an 8 1/2 x 11 envelope. It ran thirty pages.

Jimmy and I had a serious talk with Bobby that night about his purchasing prowess. Despite Bobby promising never to do it again, we took his device and set the parental controls. Unbelievably, Bobby did the same thing the following year! This time he ordered one hundred and forty videos, four less. (Inadvertently, he lost Wi-Fi one day. When I reset it, I forgot to turn the parental controls back on.)

Bobby is all about Bobby. Life takes place in *his* world only. I not only think he is self-centered, but I also think Bobby is self-absorbed! It is not his fault; it's just the way his mind works. At a buffet luncheon once, my mother-in-law noticed him coming back to the table with a delicious-looking dessert. With eager anticipation, she spoke up.

"Bobby, that looks good. Nana would love a piece like that."

"Help yourself," he replied, "it's over there, on the table."

"What's the matter with you?" he thinks. "You have two legs!"

Bobby is all set; you're on your own. Even if *I* hinted at a piece, he probably would have said the same thing to me.

While this self-centeredness might be a characteristic of autism, I don't think Bobby knows he's autistic. I honestly don't believe he suspects there is anything wrong with him or with the fact that he is still relying on us into his forties. Periodically, he queries, "Promise me you'll always take care of me." I did not want to cross that bridge but decided to test the waters.

"Bobby," I began, "everyone's left home except you."

"So?" he replied. (No siblings around, the whole upstairs and us to himself? Ideal!)

"Well, Bobby," I went on, "You're getting older, and when people grow up, like your brothers and sisters, they find a job and move into an apartment. Others have roommates and staff who are always there to take care of them. You wouldn't have to worry about anything."

That explanation might have helped Bobby, but to picture Bobby living anywhere else was utterly unfathomable to both Jimmy and me. My day-to-day routines to keep Bobby's life manageable are extensive enough; what about all the little things I do: cleaning his glasses, emptying his razor, having a snack ready when he comes home? On and on the list goes. I was overwhelmed just thinking of the avalanche of changes he would face. How would he manage if those things were left undone, not to mention what living in a new house with strangers would entail?

But we knew that transitioning Bobby to a group home had to happen. Our three-story home was too big, and the upkeep meant Jimmy never stopped. Secretly too, I harbored a dream of moving to an over fifty-five community. But that would not happen any time soon – Bobby was only forty.

At twenty-two, when Bobby transitioned to "Adult Services," we put him onto the DDS list for residential housing. Years passed. I sensed that nothing was going to move forward unless I moved it. Now in his thirties, I contacted DDS with nervous curiosity.

"Bobby is getting older, and so are we," I began. Then I managed to ask, "Where is our name on the housing list?"

"The list," his case manager stated, "doesn't exist anymore. Instead, people are prioritized for housing based on need."

Okay, I thought. No list. Phew! I don't have to think about housing coming anytime soon.

We did, however, prepare. First, we decided to see how Bobby would fare being away from us. We signed him up for a weekend of respite care at The Friendship Home and dropped him off on a Friday evening. Back home, we waited. No calls that night, but sure enough, the phone rang early the next morning.

The staff told me that they had reserved special seating for a morning movie. They tried knocking several times on Bobby's bedroom door. He was awake but refused to come out, shouting, "I don't get up until nine o'clock on Saturdays!" I often think that Bobby's brain is like a computer – programmed.

That weekend was a tryout for him, but it was also an eye-opener for us. Our lives orbited around Bobby 24/7, 365 days a year for over 35 years. And now, gone was the strict regimen. We found ourselves acting like kids in a candy store. "What are we gonna do?" We're not on the clock! We can come and go as we want – eat what we want and when we want!"

Bobby arrived home after the weekend grinning. Gladly, we signed him up for more. We watched as he found his footing. He even branched out to attend their monthly "Guys Night" and "Theme Party Night."

Years streamed by. Respite care continued. Suddenly, however, my husband began enduring numerous medical emergencies, finally ending with a triple bypass. Before Jimmy came home from this surgery, I knew I had to talk with Bobby. Too many times, I had witnessed Bobby come up behind Jimmy and, for no apparent reason, whack him hard on the back. After our chat, Bobby said he understood that he could not touch his father. But, one day, early in his recovery, Jimmy came up from the basement and unintentionally surprised Bobby. When the basement door opened, Bobby was so startled he lashed out and shoved Jimmy against the table.

I knew then that the time had come. But where would we start? Bobby was now forty. It had been ten years since we last contacted DDS. Neither of us wanted to make the call but knew we had to.

His caseworker grasped the urgency. He also knew Bobby – all about Bobby. A little over a year later, a room in a group home became available. It suddenly became real. Nobody can ever be ready for this.

Jimmy and I visited the house and met the staff. We filled out packets of forms, collected documents, and made many, many phone calls back and forth. I also prepared questions. (Fortunately for us, transitioning took months.)

1. How much experience does the staff have working with in-dividuals with disabilities? Autism in particular? (No experience.)

2. How does the agency help transition the individual from his home to the new residential facility? (With the help of DDS.)

3. What kind of training does the staff receive? How often are they on duty? (Lots of training; someone is always there.)

4. What is the staff turnover rate? Staff to resident ratio? (Long-term staff, one has been there thirteen years. Staff ratio 2:4.)

5. How does the staff deal with emergencies? (Address with the house manager.)

6. How structured is the schedule? What does the schedule look like? (No need for a structured schedule at this time.)

7. Is there a system in place to deal with behavioral issues? (No, but a behavior plan can be set up if needed.)

8. What activities take place both in and out of the home? Is there any interaction with the community at large? (Lots of social activities regularly.)

9. What clinical staff do you have? (Full-time behaviorist on staff 24/7 and a nurse who comes two times/month.)

10. What is the situation with day programs/vocational ser-vices/life skills training? (Answer? Every individual's needs are met.)

We were encouraged by their answers and slowly became convinced we were doing the right thing.

In October 2019, eight of his "team members" gathered to discuss the details of this two-month transition. It included several dinner dates with his new housemates and a few trial overnights. It also had the (dreaded) date of informing Bobby that he was moving out. Lastly, we scheduled January 9, 2019, as the (unthinkable) moving date.

We had no clue how to present this to Bobby, but his service coordinator, Justin, decided that he and the behaviorist for DDS, Dr. Juna, would come to the house. I was relieved knowing how seriously Bobby listens to those in authority. Dr. Juna recommended putting together a "social story." She suggested it be a booklet that would explain the *"what, where, when, and how"* of it all. This approach we knew was perfect for Bobby.

We were all set. All except the hard part. The night before our meeting, I sat Bobby down and began:

"Justin and a doctor from his office will be coming tomorrow. They want to talk to us about something."

Bobby was immediately suspicious.

"What do they want to talk to us about? Is it because I've been bad?"

"No"

"Well, is it because I'm moving to a new workshop?" he asked. "I hope you're still going to take care of me!"

"Dad is going to pick you up." I continued. "The meeting is here at 3:00. You have to leave the workshop early because this is an important meeting."

He walked away; I could tell he was anxious.

Soon he called out. "I hate meetings! I want to come home tomorrow and go upstairs to relax myself!"

"No, Bobby, you have to leave early with your father."

A minute later, he responded, "Give them the message that I can't make the meeting. Everybody can go to hell!"

I thought that if any violence were to come, it would be now. But Bobby went into his room. We heard him frantically pace back and forth while grunting and perseverating on phrases we could not make out. After some time, Bobby marched back in.

"If you don't want to take care of me anymore, just say so. I am fine with that. I'll just move on."

With that, he turned and walked out. I was speechless.

The next morning Bobby seemed unusually calm even when I reminded him that he would be picked up early. Things did not go smoothly that afternoon. Bobby refused to come out despite endless coaxing from his father and staff. He stood in the doorway repeating, "I hate meetings! I hate meetings!" He would not budge. They waited. Suddenly, when the clock struck three, his usual departure time, he exited the building and strolled to the car. Bobby was fidgety on the drive home. He began reiterating what he said in the doorway, adding a little more color, "I hate f****** meetings! I hate f****** meetings!" Jimmy could only keep his eyes on the road and hope things would not escalate.

We were all was assembled in the kitchen when the back door opened. Bobby seemed nervous facing us but remained quiet and pulled up a chair. Soon, he leaned in and listened intently to everything Justin and Dr. Juna had to say. They were professional and matter of fact, just the way Bobby needed to hear about the new home.

After talking about the dinners and overnights, we presented the "social story." Bobby gobbled it up. From that meeting on, he carried the story everywhere, tucking it inside his bulging ruck-sack, which has held his treasures since he was four. From morn-ing till night, he studied the timeline and pored over the pictures.

Scouring our calendar, he spotted the date for his first house visit and turned to me. "Do you think you and Dad might change your mind and let me stay here?" I emphasized that we loved him very much but that this move was going forward. "You can call us anytime."

Some weeks later, his workplace phoned, saying, "Bobby re-fuses to leave." I asked to speak to him, but nothing would get him to the phone. Slumped in his seat, Bobby could only repeat, "Too many changes, too many changes!"

"Send the van on," I said. "I'll come to pick him up."

When I arrived, a tearful Bobby was standing at the front door with a blank stare. He suffered the long walk to the car and climbed in. In between his refrain, "Too many changes," he asked, "Why do I have to go to the group home? Why can't you take care of me anymore?" I reminded him, "You're a grownup now; it's time to move into your own place." By the time we got home, he seemed calmer. Surprisingly, he never refused to get on the van again.

The day came for that first visit. Jimmy, Bobby, and I had a quiet ride over. We entered the living room where his other house-mates were sitting. Out of the blue, Bobby walked over to each of them, shook their hands, and said, "Hi! I'm Bobby." I never saw Bobby do this before and would not have suggested it knowing his aversion to touch. I had to ask myself, "Is this my son?" Jimmy and I left for a quick bite and returned with such trepidation. Out came Bobby smiling.

After each visit, I asked how it went. Bobby would only regale me with what he had to eat. For the next eight weeks, all six visits went off without incident. Bobby never mentioned the move to us, but sometimes he would ask about staying. When I said, "No," he countered, "Well, if you ever change your mind, just let me know."

Just before Bobby was to move, I asked to attend a staff meeting at his house. I wanted to greet each caregiver personally and paint the broadest picture of Bobby I could, including helpful hints about his idiosyncrasies and my well-used tricks to manage them. It was on the drive home from that meeting that a mysterious calm washed over me. I finally knew I had done all I could.

Moving day neared. I reviewed the plan for the day with Bobby and promised that we would all go out for his favorite meal before we drove to his new home. On January 9, for the last time, Bobby stepped out of our house into the unknown. I watched from the front door as he and his father walked away. Suddenly, he turned around to face me.

"Are you sure I have to go?"

He hesitated for a moment and went on. "I thought I could

25

talk you out of it, but I guess not."

I swallowed my tears. Bobby could not see our two hearts breaking.

The three of us had an unhurried drive over, and without any to-do, Bobby opened the door to his new home and sat calmly on the living room couch while I unpacked the rest of his things. My husband had to step outside to hide his tears.

Bobby's room is ideal. It's off by itself with its own bathroom. We furnished it with a new bed, bedspread, curtains, area rug, and TV. It felt homey. Bobby seemed comfortable. When the last things were put away, and the room tidied up, it was time for us to leave. So, I kissed him goodbye and then smiled weakly.

"Bye, Honey, I'll call you."

"Call me tomorrow night," he uttered.

The door closed behind us. That was that.

In our forty-two years together, this was the biggest challenge of our married life, and with five children, we have faced some big tests! Nothing about this, not one thing, was easy. We know it's right, but that does not make the sadness go away.

We try to stay on top of things at his new home. But when I went to switch out his winter clothes for summer ones, I opened the door to his room and froze. The floor was covered with dust balls, and his new red, white, and blue quilt with matching pillow shams had bled together. I was not happy. I pulled the quilt down and found his top sheet rolled up in a ball between the two pillows. (Bobby thinks if you cover it up, nobody will ever know.)

My complaint was not only about *those* sorry sights but about my expectations. I was under the impression that Bobby would be shown how to participate in the house routines the moment he arrived. Management heard me, and things have improved.

Despite this initial setback, we are pleased with the staff and the house. Michaela, the interim house manager, has Bobby's number. She knows how to talk to him and, better yet, how to handle him. Ann, the woman who does the cooking, is great too. She has a beautiful calming effect and seems confident in her role. Right away, she informed us that she does not buy junk food and cooks with organic items when possible. It had to be true. In just a few months, Bobby lost sixteen pounds. The staff were thrilled and wanted to get him something special. Excitedly at dinner one night, they presented their gift. Bobby opened the envelope, saw tickets to the Celtics' playoff game, and in all earnestness said, "I'd rather not go. *Monday Night Raw* is on then. Could you please call them and ask if they could reschedule it?" he added.

Bobby is still Bobby. But he is maturing. An animated Michaela recently called exclaiming, "You should be so proud! Bobby advocated for himself." We see that he is also picking up new habits. He came for his first overnight announcing, "I have coffee with my breakfast every morning, you know." On the ride home, Jimmy decided to take him to Dunkin' Donuts. Bobby stepped up and ordered his coffee.

"How would you like that?" the server asked.

"In a cup," Bobby answered.

Like most adults, Bobby wears a watch. He insists on wearing it even though we see it balancing on his wrist, the band shredding more each day. When it lets go and drops to the floor, Bobby simply picks it up and lays it back on his wrist. We have a standby watch, and I have offered to buy a new one many times, but he refuses. Santa did bring him one. He was happy but said he would keep the old one because "it's still working." Bobby takes the watch off at night but sleeps with the other one in his hand. Watches, clocks, and calendars have helped Bobby keep his life well ordered.

In the five months he has been gone, we have had him for four overnights. His odd behaviors have calmed down significantly, but they do not go away. Every so often, I catch him flapping or saying weird things to himself. I look over at him quizzically. He had a telling response for me once.

"A son like me needs to do that sometimes."

I said, "okay" and smiled at all that reveals.

He is upbeat when he visits, politely thanks us for "a nice day," and adds, "You're going to have me for more weekends, right?"

We see other signs of him stretching into adulthood. As much as we think that Bobby lives in his bubble, he now surprises us with questions about current events. He will mention celebrities like the ones in the news recently – Bill Cosby and Kevin Spacey – and asks if they did something wrong. Often, after hearing about somebody getting shot, stabbed, or beaten up, he'll ask, "What did they do to deserve that?"

His curiosity now even extends beyond the news. We over-heard him talk to "Alexa" in his bedroom. He treats *her* like a good friend and his personal encyclopedia.

"Alexa, why do people get headaches?" he'll ask.

"I don't know the answer to that question," she replies. "You should contact WebMD."

Even when *she* can't come up with an answer, he doesn't get frustrated. Instead, he moves on, "Alexa, how do you spell, 'wrestling?'" Or "Alexa, is Ben Stiller still a good actor?"

Actors have become a curiosity, but he has not lost his penchant for music. He asks Alexa for songs by new performers – artists and songs we didn't even know he knew. I've found myself asking, "Bobby, who's singing that?" or "I didn't know that person sang that!" His recollection of auditory and visual things continues to astound us.

Having Bobby with us for a night is both heartwarming and challenging. Each time Jimmy drops him back home, he is nearly in tears, saying, "I hate this because now we are both sad all over again." I have toyed with the idea of keeping Bobby two nights but have been warned not to interfere with this "adjustment stage." My daughter, Julie, a nurse in the field of Human Services, cautioned us, saying, "That's a mistake people make. Group home activities need to be experienced together so that roommates bond," she advised. "Given too many home visits, they do not want to go back."

Bobby always leaves us with the same reminder: "Now don't forget, call me Monday, Wednesday, and Friday at 8 o'clock." The other night I called at 7:55. He did not pick up.

When I reach him, the first thing I hear is his thunderous holler: "HELLOOOO."

"Hi Honey," I giggle.

"Oh, hi Mom, thanks for calling me; I like hearing the sound of your voice."

"How was your day?" (Of course, it's up to me to make all the conversation.)

"Well, I was good at the house."

"What about your work program?"

"I'm sorry to tell you, but I didn't have a very good day; I did some teasing."

"Bobby, I'm disappointed."

"Sorry to give you the upsetting news, but I had to tell you the truth."

"What about the rest of the week?" I ask.

"I'll be good tomorrow and will have four good days, I promise."

"Okay, we'll see."

Bobby has a propensity to taunt his co-workers in a not-so-nice way. Our old behavior charts with the checks and happy faces? They have not followed him to work, but staff notes his antics in a "communication book" that goes back and forth. He hates it when bad behaviors are written for us to see. I have caught him on occasion fumbling about, attempting to scratch out the rotten note or rip the whole page out.

"Bobby, what's up?" I ask.

"Oh," he stammers, "I guess they forgot to write in my notebook today."

It has taken a while, but Bobby finally participates in some of the house's social activities. For months, he would tell staff, "I'd rather not go, I'll wait here." When he relayed this to me, I explained, "Bobby, you need to go along with the guys. If you do not go, they have to leave a staff person behind, and I am sure all staff wants to go. It's not fair!" Happily, he called a few days later. "We went to a cookout. I went like you wanted me to and had a good time."

Generally, Bobby will not participate because he does not know what to expect. You can't just tell him, "We're going to a cookout." His anxiety ratchets up. He can't form the questions to ask, so it is easier for him just to say, "No thanks." It's all in the details: "We're going to leave at noon for a cookout in Weymouth, and we'll be back around five." Maybe you should also know what is being served.

Despite his extreme anxiety, he is managing this major change and growing closer to his housemates. He now enters his new home to a distant but loud reception.

"Hey Bobby, welcome home!"

"I'm baaaack!" he singsongs.

I catch a glimpse of the funny Bobby I know as he strolls into the kitchen, stands up tall, and announces, "Here I am."

I keep a picture of Bobby at work. I probably shouldn't. It's been over a year, but most times, when we talk, he says, "Do you know what I think about every day? How much I miss living with you." He might also sneak in, "Is the house quiet without me?" But when he says, "How come mothers stop taking care of their children?" my heart drops. I have to stick to my script. Jimmy continues to well up at the mere mention of Bobby's name, and both of us think the separation is never going to get easier.

Jimmy and I love to talk about Bobby, but not many people want to hear it. I don't think they understand how fascinating he is and how interesting life has been with him. Perhaps they believe there is not much going on with someone who has autism. A pediatrician early on told me Bobby would never love and would most likely be institutionalized.

Bobby used to say, "Thank you" when I told him I loved him, meaning "Thank you for loving me." I finally challenged him, asking "Don't you love me back?" Finally, I heard it. "I love you too." My heart swells each time I hear it. Jimmy asks, "How come you can't say that to me?" Bobby replies, "Just my mother."

He still cannot allow me to hug him, but a while ago, when sitting down, he came up behind me and said, "I just want to rub faces." He leaned down and pressed one of his cheeks against mine. Bobby does this now each time he visits. I will take all his affectionate displays.

Since he was born, Bobby has made me laugh every day, several times a day. Even with all the stress and the years of negative behaviors, I have laughed. And despite the hard work, he has brought us such joy. Our lives would have been incomplete without him.

Dawn and Sean & Jenna

Fragile X Siblings

I was young – and naïve – when I had my children. I met my husband-to-be, Stephen, in junior high. He was the class clown and extremely popular; I was the timid, reserved girl. At the age of thirteen, we became an item.

At eighteen, against my parent's wishes, I moved out of their home and into his apartment. That next November, in 1976, we married. Ten months later, I had my first son, Steve. Two and a half years later, I gave birth to Sean. Jenna arrived in 1982, followed in 1989 by Jared, who evened out our family.

Steve was such a manageable baby that when Sean arrived with colic, I was thrown. I could not get anything done. I solicited the help of my mother, who devised an ingenious trick. She put a baby seat in his carriage and attached a long rope to the handle. With a gentle push, I could watch Sean and the stroller glide down our long kitchen corridor. Just as easily, I could draw it back. I was able to cook and clean while Sean, now quiet and content, rolled along.

Sean was a cute baby and made us laugh a lot. But he also had some strange behaviors. Most toddlers cry when you put them to bed; Sean cried to *go* to bed. He also had frequent fits; he would drop to the floor and begin screaming and kicking. Behaviors were one thing; developmental milestones were another. He was late learning to walk. In truth, he did not walk and instead ran at fourteen months. I had to hold him by the hand whenever we went out. Often, he would scratch, even bite to let him go. I was not always clear about what triggered his angst or what made him run.

I mentioned these idiosyncrasies to my pediatrician. He identified Sean as having "Minimum Brain Dysfunction (MBD)." Later, he added another diagnosis – "attention deficit hyperactivity disorder (ADHD)." Given that second diagnosis, Sean was prescribed Ritalin. As a result, I would find him sitting on a basketball at the end of our driveway, mesmerized by the traffic going by. The Ritalin had to go.

Between Sean's colic and these two diagnoses, the writing was on the wall. I sensed I was in for a few challenges. Peculiarities kept surfacing, fear of dogs for example. Sean had a second sense about them. Even before I could see one, he would begin climbing up my side. I did not understand his fear since we owned dogs, and nothing ever happened. To this day, he is cautious around them but loves our eighty-pound puppy, Contessa.

Sean was also intrigued by my niece's long, dark hair. As a three-year-old, he was drawn to *playing* with it, or so we thought. He didn't pull it or hurt her, but he flicked at it with odd, quick hand movements. I was to learn it was the beginning of him "flapping." (Flapping is a self-stimulatory behavior often associated with autism. Rocking, head-banging, scratching, or biting one are others.)

At the age of four, Sean could say a handful of words, but could not form sentences. He was placed in a neighboring town's special needs pre-school where they concentrated on managing his behaviors. His graduation day was memorable. Sean's teacher, Mrs. Cahill, held on to Sean's hand the entire ceremony. She knew he would dart; she also knew he was fast! People probably did not notice her tight grip; they were captivated by his endearing antics.

Practically sewn to Mrs. Cahill's side, Sean managed to salute everyone who entered using his free hand – elbow out and index finger to the forehead.

He was becoming "*Mr. Personality*" in school, but at home, his temper tantrums were mounting. My pediatrician never seemed alarmed but saw that I was. He suggested I take Sean to a neurologist, who found nothing. We carried on.

Sean received auxiliary services in elementary school, including speech. But his vocabulary did not increase, and he had difficulty expressing himself. His grandmother used to say, "Oh, he's tongue-tied. He just needs to have that tongue snipped." At five or six, his speech teacher asked him to repeat the rhyme, "To market, to market to buy a fat pig." Sean replied, "To *the* market. To *the* market." No matter how she tried, he could not reproduce it.

Often, his way of communicating could be equally odd. He would cite random idioms at just the right time. Once, I took Sean to see my grandmother after her leg was amputated. Leaving, I asked, "What did you think of Nana Margaret?" Without hesitating, he answered, "She doesn't have a leg to stand on!"

Years passed. With that came increased sensitivities and more unusual behaviors. Sean could not look anyone in the eye, loud noises disturbed him, and crowds made him wail. The circus came to town. My mother took the grandkids to watch it spring to life. Sean seemed to enjoy the tents going up, but the clamor of it all tormented him. They had to leave.

Neither his pediatrician nor his neurologist ever batted an eye at these stories. I was sure something else was going on. One day, worn down and weary, I sat on the couch and flipped through the TV channels. I happened on an Oprah Winfrey show. The guests included a married couple and their family of seven. Each child was diagnosed with something called Fragile X syndrome. As the parents described the characteristics, I realized they were all too familiar. Large heads, they pointed out, with long faces and sizable protruding ears. The parents talked about speech issues, anxiety, persistent hand flapping, and Presto! I didn't know whether to laugh or cry. Oprah and I just diagnosed Sean.

Back to the neurologist's office I went, filled with new facts and hope. Maybe, just maybe, there was a treatment. Incredulous, the doctor looked through his notes and said, "I must have overlooked it." Sean was tested. The conclusion? Sean has Fragile X syndrome (FXS). It was a long twelve years but finally, I got a name for my son's troubles.

Naturally, I set out to find out all I could about FXS. I discovered a Dr. Randi J. Hagerman, the leader in Fragile X research and signed up for his "Randi's Group" monthly mailings which included information, research, and phone numbers of other mothers with children diagnosed with FXS. (Dr. Hagerman is currently the director of the Fragile X Research and Treatment Center in Davis, CA.)

I learned that Fragile X syndrome stems from a mutation in a single gene called FMR1. I also discovered that FXS can include a mild to severe intellectual disability and that males are more affected than females. I connected with a few of the mothers on the phone list and when researchers proclaimed that there would be a cure within five years, we were spurred on by such hope. But each passing year that hope dimmed until it finally disappeared. There has never been a cure. Fragile "Hex," I thought.

I brought news of Sean's diagnosis to his teachers only to see their brows furrow. I wanted them to listen to all I knew about Fragile X, but schools at the time were grappling with this new label, "Autism."

Our neurologist hitched us up with a team of researchers at Boston University who were interested in finding the origin of the gene in our family. Despite numerous DNA samples from all family members, they could only report that my father, sister, and I are carriers.

I asked if being a *"carrier"* meant that I *have* Fragile X. "Yes," they said, "but there are degrees. Those with this gene might not appear different, but they often display characteristics of the syndrome." I began to think of my family. My father, while withdrawn and self-centered is generous to a fault. As he ages, he has significant mood swings and signs of hypochondria. These, I am told, are textbook symptoms of older men with this gene. I have features too – social anxiety, low self-esteem, and word re-trieval issues. But news that these shortcomings were caused by a gene brought such a sigh of relief. I began to look at the world differently and have worked to overcome those challenges.

It was through a blood test that I learned my ten-year-old daughter, Jenna, has Fragile X syndrome too. We would not have guessed it for her because she is quite different from Sean. Jenna was not hyperactive, and she did not have behavior issues; in fact, she was an easy baby. But even before her diagnosis, things gave me pause. For one, she was slower in reaching her milestones than Sean. She did not walk until she was eighteen months. At age four, she could only utter three words. Her speech might have improved quicker than Sean's, but that was hard to tell. She was extremely timid and not at all talkative. Since I was the same way at her age, I assumed her bashfulness was hereditary. Without knowing about Fragile X, I went ahead and signed her up for regular pre-school.

Jenna made a few friends and seemed happy enough, but her teacher soon let on that she had fallen behind and suggested I have her evaluated. Again, I knew Jenna was slower but assumed it stemmed from that painful introversion. The anxiety it stirred up was visible at school. We watched as her nursery schoolteacher instructed the class to march onto the stage. That alone would have terrified her. But then, one by one, they were asked to introduce themselves. When it was Jenna's turn, she vanished behind the preschooler next to her.

Jenna was not only shy in school, she was reticent anywhere

we went. If anyone stopped us walking, Jenna stuck to me as if we were surgically attached. If they asked her a question, more than likely, she would not answer and avert her eyes to that place far away.

Before entering kindergarten, I took the preschool's suggestion and had Jenna evaluated. The tests determined that she has a borderline IQ. Despite that, she was placed in a regular class. Quickly, it was decided that she, like Sean, needed "*special services.*" Both received speech therapy, occupational therapy, and "*academic support*" for money and math. Over time, Jenna benefited from all those services. (Sean less so. He still cannot understand basic math or money concepts or tie his shoes, but he loves to gab, and with anyone!)

Even knowing that Jenna was an introvert with a borderline IQ, there were indications that something was still not right. One evening, we went to pick up her brother, Steve, from football practice and parked near the field to wait. While she hopped between the front and back seat, she looked over to the driver next to us and shouted, "Hi!" The woman responded in such a deep voice that Jenna was taken aback. "Are you a man or a woman?" she blurted out.

On another day we stopped in a bakery. Jenna observed the saleswoman who had an unfortunate case of acne. Suddenly Jenna queried, "What's all over your face?" I tried stepping on her foot, but immediately she turned to me, "Why are you stepping on my foot?" My suspicions were answered. Jenna neither understood social cues nor had any filters.

Nonetheless, she was easy to raise, that is until *she* realized something was wrong with her. And the hints piled up. When taken out for "*specials,*" she would turn crimson noting that her friends didn't come; they stayed in class. She was also quick to see classmates do things she could not. She tried playing soccer in elementary school but was not terribly agile, and therefore, not particularly good. (Poor coordination can be a characteristic of FXS.) Despite these blows to her self-esteem, she still enjoyed going to school. She joined Brownies and even invited friends over. It was then that I saw firsthand where Jenna lagged behind. Her language skills were inferior, her math skills were practically nonexistent, and she could not grasp money concepts.

Jenna's growing self-awareness convinced her that she did not measure up. What little self-esteem she had was marred by years of ruthless teasing. The result? Slowly but surely, Jenna became so self-conscious she would not leave home except to go to school. And there, she withdrew from everyone.

By seventh grade, it worsened; Jenna became nonverbal. One afternoon, she flew in the door, dropped her books, ran to the bathroom, and vomited – violently. She was so sick yet so afraid to speak up in class. My concern grew. I suggested she try medication, but Jenna adamantly refused. The bullying continued.

Kids can be cruel, but so, I learned, can teachers. Her speech therapist one day yelled at her, "Look at me when I am talking to you!" Jenna came home undone. I immediately wrote the school to clarify the sensitive issues around Fragile X. "Asking a person with FXS to make eye contact induces a whole other layer of anxiety," I explained. The therapist was directed to write Jenna an apology but, by then, it was too late. Jenna completely shut down. She learned not to trust anyone. To this day, some twenty years later, even the slightest look can unravel her. Teasing does not offend Sean in the same way. He blows it off with hand gestures and walks away. Even so, I have heard him say, "I don't like that person." He cannot answer when I ask, "Why," but I sense they said something derogatory to him, and it stuck. Both Sean and Jenna know rejection.

After junior high, Jenna was placed in a *significantly separate program* in our local high school. She came home telling me that she was less a student in the class and more an aide – reading to others and taking classmates to the bathroom. We moved her to a neighboring special needs program where she learned functional academics and vocational skills. Jenna learned to read and tried to build back her self-confidence but soon announced, "I think I want to try medication." After a few weeks, she came to me, "I should have done this a long time ago. This medication makes me feel like a regular person."

Sean was already in our high school's special needs program, but unlike Jenna, it worked for him. For one, Sean was outgoing and thrived knowing everyone in the school not only by their first name but their last as well. You would see him "*high five*" fellow students and then add his unique (nonsense) greeting, "Pot of leaves!" or "annnnk" (grunt) "Peanut butter!" In a short time, Sean began making up names for people which only endeared him more to them. He never referred to his younger brother by name, instead Jared is "The Little One." Jenna is the "Cat's Ass," and all the cousins have names: "Little Yakka," "Moose," "Sport."

Urged on by members of the football team, Sean signed up to be their water boy. He loved suiting up for the games, but when I returned to pick him up, there he was – *Mr. Social*. His helmet was off, and he was strolling up and down the sidelines, chatting with spectators lounging on the grass. He never played in a game but went to them all just to "*hang out with the guys*." Sean did not want to socialize with "those special needs kids." He never thought of himself as different even though he spent each of his twenty-two school years in special needs classrooms.

In his last year, Sean got all spiffed up to go to the senior prom. Sadly, he went by himself. When he heard his name read over the loudspeaker, he entered the gussied-up gym to the roar of the seniors. They were cheering and chanting his nickname, "Meaty... Meaty...." The class president quickly took the mike. "We want to thank Sean Nisby for his great catchphrases." Sean was voted "Most Popular," and still points it out under his name in the yearbook.

That June, Sean's BMOC career ended. It was as if overnight, everything came to an abrupt halt – everything except his tantrums. He wouldn't dare have those fits at school or in public, but his sizzling temper led to fiery flareups at home. Scary given the fact that he was that much stronger now. His anger was fueled by unrelenting anxiety. Doctors were treating it, but the medication stopped working. Sean was now hitting walls.

I decided to take him to a different psychiatrist who began, "Sean, do you ever feel sad or mad?" I tried explaining that Sean does not understand a question like that. The doctor kept at it but, not getting too far, finally conceded. He then started writing his notes. Sean stood behind him, making the gesture for slitting one's throat. "Let's get outta here!" his eyes begged.

The psychiatrist did change Sean's antidepressant. And in a few weeks, he added Depakote to ease his outbursts and Topamax to stabilize his mood. Sean had gone from being on one pill a day to three, twice a day. This would have been impossible for him to manage alone, so he now has a pillbox that *I* need to remember to set up each week. I still see terrible anger.

Jenna, on the other hand, has conquered so many adversities. She came out of her shell, which boosted her self-esteem. At twenty-two when her high school days ended, Jenna was ready to move on. She went to work in a daycare center through Brockton Area Multi-Service Industries (BAMSI). Jenna enjoyed the little ones and loved the staff, but over time her hours shrank from four to three to two and then to one. The twenty-five-minute drive to get there was eventually not worth it.

Jenna transferred to another agency, Road to Responsibility (RTR.) For the last several years, three days a week, she has been their receptionist. Polite and appropriate now, Jenna answers busy phone lines and pages staff. She also monitors people coming into the building.

Because Jenna is always ready for a laugh, staff and clients enjoy bantering with her. Not long ago, with a crowd gathered at her desk, Jenna jumped up and began acting out the TV commercial, "*Hump Day.*" Shy Jenna? She made such a hit that a staff member bought her a stuffed camel. Eagerly now, she waits for Wednesdays to reach into her desk drawer and set it in full view. Jenna was recently offered a receptionist job for the other two days. Ecstatic after her first day, she flew in the door exclaiming, "They say I'm the best!"

Not long after Sean graduated, my husband found him a job with the International Brotherhood of Electrical Workers (IBEW) working in a nearby garage. The "*yard*" was loaded with machinery. Sean was tasked with keeping tabs on each – which ones needed oil changes, what truck needed to be stocked with what parts, etc. He loved strutting around with the bosses and informing them, "Number 23 needs bolts," or "That one needs an oil change." They were amazed; he was so accurate.

Sean's memory has always been puzzling. When he was twelve, his father called me, "Come watch what Sean can do." There on the pool table were the balls, racked with the numbers facing down. Sean rattled off each number effortlessly. It was a "Rain-Man" type of thing.

Sean also recalls curious things. Some give me the chills. He dreams about my mother, who passed away thirty-four years ago. Sean was only five.

"Nana came to see me last night."

"Oh really, what did she say?"

"She said, "You have got to stop working so hard.""

He even dreams of my great grandmother and says he remembers her coming into his room. Sean was an infant then. His dreams never shake him; they are simply incidents to him. I am comforted by the possibility that someone is watching over him.

Sean was good at this job and considered reliable. So reliable that they let him move trucks around the lots despite not having a license. He got a bit carried away. Behind my back, he drove *our* car down main roads in town. I got wind that he also took his brother's truck to Dunkin' Donuts, parallel parked it, and popped in for a cup of coffee! Another day coming home from work, I saw my son, Steve, and his coworker tear out of our driveway. They were laughing uproariously. I wondered what was so funny until I saw who followed. There was Sean, driving one of Steve's oversized landscaping trucks with a trailer attached. Sean glanced my way, and his face turned white, but he kept going. "Steve needed my help," he later explained.

Sean's father, despite my protests, bought him a two-wheeler moped and a John Deere mower. Sean is actually a good driver, but I won't let him get a license. I am afraid he will get lost or encounter a detour and not know what to do. It's all too worrisome. Fortunately, he is not pleading with me for it.

Sean's job *"with the guys"* was custom-made for him, but sadly, the business went under. Sean now goes to RTR, the same day program as Jenna. A few days a week, he goes out to community worksites on a custodial crew. Other days, Sean performs in-house assembly jobs. He is terrific on many packaging tasks, ones that, curiously, Jenna struggles to do. Neither Sean nor Jenna stresses over going to work. They both love their jobs and being at RTR.

As they were settling into their new lives, my marriage was falling apart. I knew when I married Stephan that he was an alcoholic. Living with his constant drinking was hard enough, but then came the drugs – cocaine first and then heroin. The marriage grew shakier. It collapsed when I learned that our home was in foreclosure, all because of drugs. I kick myself for not having left him a long time ago; his addictions affected us all.

After thirty-one years, I told Stephan that Jenna and I were leaving on February 1st. He did not believe us, but that morning, we gathered the bare essentials and fled. Because change is so hard for Sean, he stayed with his father and brother. I tried luring Sean with frequent overnights, but Sean could not fathom moving.

Change has always been challenging for both Sean and Jenna. I saw that when they were young. A clothes dryer ignited a fire in our kitchen once. The house was so damaged it collapsed. We lived in a trailer on the property while a new one was being built. It had a comfy living room, a kitchen area, and three good-sized bedrooms. Yet, for some unknown reason, neither Sean nor Jenna would sleep in their rooms. They chose instead to sleep in the living room across from each other on the love seats. When our house was ready, they still refused to sleep in their bedrooms. Fortunately, after a year or so, Jenna found *her* way back but not Sean. He would grab a pillow and a sleeping bag to settle in on the floor at the end of our bed. No amount of coaxing worked. I even climbed into bed with him until he fell asleep. We would find him nestled at the foot of our bed in the morning. After fourteen years of this, I was about to give up. But, one night, Sean, then nineteen, went into his room, shut the door, and turned off the light. That was that. Not long after, he came to me and said, "You're right, I love my room. I should have done it a long time ago."

The same foot-dragging was happening again. Sean could not be persuaded to leave home. His brother, Steve, who had been urging me to take him, finally packed Sean and the bulk of his clothes and drove to Scituate. The next morning, Sean stood out on the front porch, stretching as usual. And, looking out at the calm blue ocean, he declared, "Yup, my home now."

There was another catalyst in his decision. A few weeks before, with his father passed out in the living room, Sean decided to start up the John Deere in the garage. His brother, Steve, went for pizza. For some reason, the motor did not engage right away. So, Sean reached for a can of starter fluid and sprayed the engine. It sparked, triggering a small flame. Sean raced back to the house for a glass of water. The fire quickly ignited the gas tank next to it. Sean saw this and ran to the neighbors. The fire was now blazing behind him. Steve returned with the pizza just as the whole garage blew. It was so loud that my ex came to on the couch.

I did not think much when my phone rang that day; it was my birthday, after all. The news, however, sent me racing back to Abington. There, blanketing the front lawn, were numerous bystanders milling about. Sean, the proverbial mayor, wandered about greeting people he hadn't seen in a while, "Hey, how are ya?" His beloved John Deere had melted into the concrete, and all he could say to the onlookers was, "Thank God I still have the key." The fire chief questioned him but quickly realized Sean had no clue how the fire happened.

Sean settled in with Jenna and me. My soul mate, Molly (or *Kitty* as Sean affectionately calls her), also moved in with us. She has been a godsend to me, and a role model for both Sean and Jenna. To them, Molly is a "regular" person, not a parent, relative, or coworker. One of her many talents is impersonations, rib-tickling impersonations.

Sean loves to be with her. He is jazzed if Molly suggests going out somewhere. Immediately he jumps in her car. If Jenna and I decide to tag along, he climbs out. I understand. Sean wants a normal life with someone to pal around with him.

Jenna loves to joke with Molly. She is more than a friend to Jenna; she is a substitute sister. Both Sean and Jenna are unusually attentive to her. They have adapted many of Molly's charming ways, her social mannerisms, and her healthy habits.

It's outside the house that they yearn for friends. If someone is nice to either of them, they automatically think they are their *best* friend. Calls come in day and night for Jenna. But she does not want to socialize with them outside RTR. One day, however, she came home gushing about a new client. *Finally*, she thought, *I will have a friend*. Jenna arrived home the following day, dejected. The new girl's behavior was so out of control that staff had to restrain her. Sadly, there would be no friendship there; Jenna always toes the line.

Another client at RTR would love to be Jenna's friend. This young woman has an apartment, a driver's license, and a car. But Jenna is put off by her purple Mohawk. She also cannot understand why this girl spends good money on a crib for her cat and then has to beg Jenna for gas money.

Sean chums around with guys at RTR, but he likes the girls. He has never had a girlfriend, but he thinks he has. At his senior prom, Sean had his picture taken with several girls he called "*girlfriends*." He later lined the photos up in his room like trophies. These were regular senior girls, most of whom were very pretty. Today, those he calls girlfriends are from his RTR program – all have special needs. One is a 5'4" heavyset woman, another speaks in a guttural voice and calls him "Sausage."

He still loves to tell people he has a girlfriend. Not long ago, he had hernia surgery. Afterward, a nurse handed Sean his clothes. Still groggy, he managed to pipe up, "Wanna see my girlfriend?" When she said "yes," he reached into his pants pocket, pulled out a paper with a phone number on it, and thrust it forward to show her.

There seems to be plenty of names and numbers that Sean has collected, but I sense he is much too scared to even kiss a girl. Apparently, however, he has phoned several. That has led to trouble. One told a supervisor that Sean calls her saying, "Hey babe, wanna hang out?" I cannot even imagine Sean saying that, but that is what *she* says. Other girls have made it clear to staff that they "don't want to talk to him." Yet, *they* call *him* later in the day. (Oh, the drama!) I do worry. I learned that if people with Fragile X touch a girl and begin rocking, it suggests arousal. I have no idea what that could mean, nor do I want to find out.

Talking with Sean about "*girlfriend protocol*" makes him defensive. In the middle of explaining something, his voice gets louder. "Don't worry about it!" he insists.

I did not want any more trouble, so I took his phone and deleted a girl's number. He was spoken to at work for calling her again. *How did he find her number*, I wondered? I knew he would never have remembered it. Light dawned when another girl in the same group home used their house phone to call him.

Having a low IQ does not mean Sean is stupid! However, it does mean that I need to be vigilant, especially as I watch Sean become more and more uninhibited. He used to stare at girls, but these days, I catch him eyeing them more intensely. Recently I found him peeking into a neighbor's window. I told him not to be a "creeper." Angrily, Sean refused to believe that characterization probably because he is naïve and does not know what being a "creeper" means. I explained, "People don't do that; you'll make them scared." Irritated, he replied, "Okay, I won't do it again." But he does.

Jenna, on the other hand, is appropriate with males. She also had a boyfriend. It was in high school when a classmate, Eric, developed a crush on her. Finally, after ten years, he convinced Jenna to move in with him. It seemed okay to me. I would be stopping by to take them grocery shopping or out for a meal. I also knew that Eric's brother was there frequently overseeing Eric's every need. I wanted to give them a chance. They go to work every day, put a bit of money in the bank, and can easily create a life for themselves. They like going to the park, grabbing a slice of pizza, watching a local ball game, or walking up to the Depot for a meal.

Jenna enjoyed the arrangement for a while, but a year later, she asked, "Can I move back home?"

"Why do you want to do that?" I asked, surprised.

"I don't know, all he does is talk about sports."

"I'm done with relationships," Jenna reckons. I encourage her to keep her eyes open, but she quickly answers, "I am all set with men." I suspect some of that comes from seeing what I went through with her father.

Eric still calls her; their day would be incomplete without it. Occasionally, however, Jenna's facial expressions reveal her true feelings, and she lets those calls go to voicemail. Their conversations are so predictable; the words never vary:

"How was your day?"

"What did you do?"

"What are you having for supper?"

It's their world, and not much in it changes.

Sean seeks camaraderie, Jenna, kindness. My neighbors can be friendly to them. To ensure that, I made a point of going door to door to introduce myself and them. "I have two special needs kids," I explained. "My son can wear out his welcome. Just tell him, 'It's time to go home now; I have things to do.'" Each neighbor seemed receptive to that. After alerting them, I drove down the street to the small convenience store. I left my number and a warning, "My son, Sean, might hang out here, and he'll talk." Nobody has ever called me from there, but I need to keep a pulse on it. A young female employee greets him with, "Hey homey, wz up?" So, now he thinks he has a friend.

Sean did befriend one of our neighbors. He visited her often. Not long ago, he looked through her screen door, saw her on the phone, and walked in. That supposedly frightened her so much she vowed she would call the cops. She didn't. Instead, she complained to my landlord, who immediately stood up for Sean. He even left a Wikipedia page about Fragile X syndrome on her front stoop. I do not think she glanced at it. Since then, she has used the incident to scare others in the neighborhood.

Sean visits another woman nearby who tells me, "He is always respectful." Frequently she visits with a drink in her hand, and I hear Sean sing out, "It's five o'clock somewhere. Time for a cocky!"

Another day, driving down our street, I saw a cruiser parked at our house. The policeman stated that "a frightened neighbor called the station reporting that a young man was riding his bike up and down the street." The officer suggested I talk to her. He would accompany me. I tried again to explain Sean's special needs to her and emphasized that he would never hurt her. She was not at all convinced.

"If he steps in this house, I will hurt him," she threatened.

My whole attitude changed. I looked to the policeman who stood there passively and then let her have it. "If you hurt him, you will have an issue with me. I am trying to explain this to you. My kids do not have a mean bone in their bodies. They would never do anything to you intentionally."

The cop walked me home and said, "It's not illegal to ride a bike up and down the street." I wondered, *why did you keep that to yourself back there?* This neighbor too felt it necessary to alert others about the dangers of Sean.

I am always on guard. It is incredibly stressful as a parent to have to go through this, so often. Thirty years ago, I began anti-anxiety medication. I can now talk about having two special needs children without crying.

Sean and Jenna get along like any other brother and sister. Jenna can aggravate him, and he will tell her to back off, but she always watches out for him. Once in a grocery store, Sean wandered away and got stuck looking at a pretty girl. Jenna went to get him. Sean was eyed suspiciously by the girl's mom, who spoke up.

"Is he bothering you?"

"No," Jenna responded, "I'm sorry, he's my special needs brother."

How does one explain that just being you makes people uneasy?

Most people would not even know that Jenna has a disability, but both can embarrass me in public places. I explain a certain off-putting thing they do a hundred times, but it does not register. Jenna still has a propensity to stop strangers in stores or restaurants with an inappropriate question or remark. She once interrupted a mother pushing a carriage and asked how old her baby was. That might have gotten a pass until she added, "Can I hold her?"

When we run into somebody she *does* know, Jenna starts by saying, "What are ya doing? Causin' trouble?" A few seconds later, when she can't think of anything else to say, she repeats, "You causin' trouble?" It has gotten a laugh in the past, but she cannot understand that it gets old. (Jokes are hard for both Jenna and Sean. Jenna sometimes gets the gist; Sean pretends he does.)

Jenna also tends to perseverate on things, nonstop for days. It's tiresome. She will also pester Molly to perform her parodies again and again. When I say "Enough, Jenna," she will jump up and shout, "I'm moving out."

Sean, too, tends to repeat stories, usually with a peculiar nervous laugh. He also talks to himself – a lot. When I stand outside his room, I hear him speaking to so many people; I almost think he sees them.

They can both see things you don't, hear whispers you wish they didn't, and remember things in detail that you are sure never happened. Sean watches people with an odd intensity. He can then imitate them to a "*t*"- their mannerisms, voice intonations, even their laugh. Jenna is similar; she is incredibly observant. She will ask about a person from a party that happened not months ago but years before. She will give me endless clues, and when I still cannot pull a name, she will add, "Remember? She had a green shirt on."

It is not only their visual acuity that's astonishing, but they were born with other keen antennae. No matter how softly I whisper something to someone in another room, they are quick to shout a response back. They also have a heightened sensitivity to smells. Jenna can become nauseous, even gag when an onion or garlic is cut. I remember a commercial on TV for the Olive Garden. It showed table after table of mouthwatering meals. As it aired, Sean took a deep breath in through his nose, and exhaled saying, "Ahhh, doesn't that smell good, Dad?"

Both had "*tactile defense*" issues when they were young. They are better now at being touched but still prefer you not hug them. Showing emotion is one thing; speaking it is another. Sean has to be coaxed. Molly often says to Sean, "Go tell your mother that you love her." He abruptly changes the subject and blabbers on nervously. If Molly persists, "C'mon Sean, look at what she did for you," he will make his way over and say, "Thanks, Ma." But then quickly slips away. He would never get that far years ago.

One time he did say he loved me; it might have been by accident. He blurted it out after a disastrous pediatric dentist appointment. Unfortunately, his teeth are terrible. A regular dentist can barely get through a cleaning. Anything foreign going into Sean's mouth makes him gag. He has thrown up on a hygienist and has even become physical with me. Once, at a local hospital, he had to be put under for an extraction. When he woke, he was deranged. Staff called security. And with the help of several nurses and doctors, Sean was given a shot of Ketamine, (a drug used to sedate large animals.) The last time I took him to the dentist, he sensed what was coming. He ripped the IV out, screaming, "Get away from me! I am not doing this!" A team had to hold him down. Later I heard, "Sorry, I love you, mom."

I will never forget that. It can be heartbreaking to raise a child with special needs. And knowing that Sean and Jenna realize they are different makes me sad. My sadness turns to jealousy sometimes. I hear people talk about their children who went off to college and are now at some job, making X amount of money. I try not to dwell on it, though. I believe that what is in my life is meant to be and that I am not given more than I can handle.

Still, there are day-to-day challenges. They need proper meals prepared and I need to monitor their hygiene while taking care of things like cutting their finger and toenails. They also need guidance around social issues. None of this keeps me up at night, but safety issues do.

Situations crop up all the time that get me thinking. I ran a quick errand the other day and left Jenna and her young nephew alone in the car. I had to emphasize to Jenna, "Do not open the door, not for anyone, even if you think it's a policeman. Don't even roll the window down. Instead, tell them that you have to call your mother." I wonder if Jenna would be enticed by a cute boy delivering *free* pizzas without updating these warnings.

Recently I came home from work to find the flame out in our gas fireplace. I asked Sean if the maintenance man came by.

"Nope," he replied.

A little while later, Sean came back and said, "The man who was trying to light the burners...."

"Man, what man?" I screeched. "Who was here? What did he do?"

"He went down to the basement and tried pushing this thing."

"Why did you let him in and not call me? You can NOT let strangers in! Did he leave a slip? What was he driving?"

"I dunno, a van."

"Did it have writing on it?"

"I think so."

I quickly called my neighbor, who usually sees all the comings and goings.

"I did see a van," she said, "but since I called you yesterday, I didn't want to be the 'nosy neighbor' and call you again."

"Did you see any writing on the van?"

"It might have said, 'Caution' on the back," she replied.

I called my landlord to no avail. Finally, I remembered that six months ago, I received a call saying the gas company would change our meter. I plowed through papers and found that today was the day.

I worry about strangers, but I am also skeptical about those who are paid to care for Sean and Jenna. Bus drivers, for example. I was informed that one driver, well known to them both, was taking over their route. Near hysterics, they both pleaded, "Betsy can't drive us, she's *the mean* driver!" With a propensity for OCD, Jenna added, "Her van has scratch tickets on the floor. And dirty tissues everywhere. It's filthy, I'm not going with her!" When I asked Sean about Betsy, he summed it up in a word, "She's a bitch." I listened to their angst all week; Jenna ending up in tears each time.

Their first day with Betsy was indicative of what was to come. Opening the van door, she *greeted* them, saying, "I don't know why I have to pick you two up. Why can't you still be on Karen's bus? I don't want to come all the way down here to get you!"

After a week of her bullying, I stepped into action and called the company's manager. "This driver needs some serious training in special needs," I said. "Aside from treating her riders like detainees telling them, 'No coffee, no phones,' they are made to sit in silence. They're petrified. One passenger even whispered to my daughter, 'I hate her.' What's worse than her cold attitude is her nasty verbalizations. Something has to change!" It took weeks of calls and then threats to go public before she was replaced.

I am also suspicious of staff and even coworkers. One day, Sean burst through the door, saying he and his case manager were going out for Chinese food the next day. "Okay," I said, "here's a twenty." Sean must have paid for the guy's lunch; no money came back. A short time later, that same staff asked Sean if he wanted coffee. Sean handed him $5 and never saw the change.

Both have been taken advantage of. An elderly bus driver once borrowed $100 from Jenna. He told her he needed to pay his electric bill. My son, Jared, took care of retrieving that money with fury the next morning. I have warned both Sean and Jenna not to carry a lot of cash anywhere, even to the workplace. Clients have even been known to steal from others. Sean and Jenna are easy targets – for anyone.

Safety is a concern, but so is watching Sean age. Like his grandfather with Fragile X, Sean is becoming moody. He has also gotten jumpy, startling easily and often. He is now terrified of driving on the highway and begs me to take back roads. When I don't, Sean becomes the worst back-seat driver. He presses his foot down dramatically and shrieks, "Watch Out! Watch Out!" I don't get it; he has never been in a car accident.

After leaving school, Sean, the outgoing one, began withdrawing. Now, he is nearly agoraphobic. If we entice him to go out, he is his old friendly self – glad to see people and often the life of the party. But inside is a ticking time bomb, a ball of pent-up energy and anger. I see him pacing back and forth in our yard, hollering on his phone. My ex-husband told me that, one day, Sean called him eighty-nine times – always with the same complaint. "I have been stuck in the house all day." He calls to report that same thing to his brother. They both know it is not true, but they do not understand why his anger is ratcheting up. None of us do.

Sean is always on his phone but will not call me for anything. If I ever call him to ask *his* whereabouts, he becomes incensed. He immediately hangs up and deletes my number. Yet, he says the sweetest things to me, knowing deep down that I am the one who is there for him, always.

I see his frustrations mount, and his anxieties grow. The last straw came when Sean hit Molly. It was scary. Yet, fifteen minutes later, he apologized, saying he didn't mean it. I called Joanna, Sean's (new) caseworker at DDS (Department of Developmental Services). I made it clear that I work more than forty hours a week and do not like leaving Sean home anymore.

Sean lacks the skills to live on his own. He does not know how to keep on top of his needs. He brings home a small paycheck but cannot add coins or figure change. The only thing he thinks he needs to know is that his morning coffee costs $3 and (unfortunately) a pack of cigarettes is $10.

Years ago, I broached the subject of a group home with him. He met the idea with anger and disdain. Even family members asked, "How can you do that?" I had to brave the conversation again.

"Sean, I am getting older and want someone to watch out for you."

I went on. "Dad can't take you in; he doesn't have the room."

"I know Ma! I know!" he chafed.

The enticement came to me. "You'd have your own room."

"Ahh," he sighed, "Peace and quiet!"

Joanna agreed that Sean needed to be in a fully staffed living situation. She was kind enough to ask if I would like *support services* until a room in a group home is available. Are you kidding me? Someone to take him out for a couple of hours? I was thrilled for the help and grateful that she understood.

In no time I received an official letter from DDS deeming him *"eligible for Residential Services."* He is even *"Priority One."* A new path lies ahead.

Jenna is easier to live with and such a help around the house. She has come so far, but things in her life are not quite right. Jenna needs more outside activities. She would benefit, too, from a job in the community where she would be around people on her level. She could also use a friend or two. All sound doable, but bullying scars linger; even the thought of attending a yoga class makes her wary. Unfortunately, she prefers to sit home and eat – another concern.

Jenna has more skills than Sean. She is a competent house-keeper; she sees things that need to be done, and for the most part, she's tidy and neat. She reads well, she cooks and has learned to handle money, at least better than she used to. If we shop and the items total fifty-three dollars, Jenna will pull three twenties from her wallet. Then she looks to me for approval.

Jenna says she would love to move to a group home. Her case manager thinks that a supervised *"independent living"* arrangement is best. But Jenna's debilitating anxiety rules that out, as do her panic attacks. These attacks are new, and their cause remains unknown. When I think back, I wonder if she had them earlier. In elementary school, she could not explain what happened. She could only say, "My heart is beating really fast." Perhaps they, too, contributed to her becoming nonverbal.

Jenna's odd eating habits also call for supervision. Getting her to eat a nutritious meal can be a challenge. Jenna likes chicken and fish but only cooked one way. She has never eaten a salad in her life and the only vegetable she eats is corn. I nag, "Try it, Jenna." She will take a bite and say, "it's all right," but does not touch it again, so I hand her a vitamin.

Looking at Sean, you would not think he eats much of anything, but he loves food, all food! I think he is hungry all the time, but that overgenerous side of Fragile X is apparent at his workplace. He regularly gives away his snack and often, his lunch. He is not fussy when it comes to food, but he is a bit quirky. He will tell you that he hates cheese, yet he lives on pizza and lasagna.

My goal is to see them both in group homes. And once there, I dream that Sean finds peace and Jenna – her niche. What heartens me most is knowing that my Fragile X's will have each other to grow old with.

Jackie and Matthew

Asperger's Syndrome

There was never any doubt growing up. I knew I wanted to work with children. So, when the time came to decide on a career, I chose to teach. My degree in Early Childhood Education prepared me for the classroom – never would I have guessed how important it would be when I had my first child.

I was passionate about educating first graders. But after five years, I left the classroom to start a family. In 1974, my husband Richard and I welcomed Matthew into our lives. He was perfect in every way.

There were, however, a few hiccups. Matthew was not your usual "rock-a-bye baby." He would often stiffen up when being held. And those baby hugs I so anticipated? They did not come. Matthew would rebuff anyone reaching out to touch him unless it was Mommy and Daddy. I didn't see that with other babies. They might be fussy about who holds them, but most of the time, a warm blanket will do! Thankfully, that rigidity softened a bit by the time Matthew turned two. He began accepting hugs. And sometimes, his teeny, little hands would start patting *your* back.

Matthew met all the developmental milestones. He never crawled, however. He stood instead and away he walked. He was not a difficult baby, but he was a finicky eater! Particular tastes and soft food textures like soup or mashed potatoes threw him. Matthew never fussed with what was put in front of him because he simply pushed it aside. And he was firm. Eventually, I knew what to feed him, but I had to learn that the hard way.

Food was one thing, noise was another. As a youngster, Matthew could not bear the sound of a vacuum. Each time we visited my mother, he would have to check all the closets to ensure the vacuum cleaner was stored away correctly.

While we knew these behaviors were different, even odd, there was a more looming concern – Matthew's inability to talk. At the age of two, he motioned for things, but his utterances were simply gibberish. Richard and I decided that listening to him was a bit like trying to learn a foreign language. So, we played along using his words, comforted that he understood ours. I worked feverishly to build on those. "Matthew, go into the kitchen, please. Find the banana on the counter and bring it to Mommy?" Each successful hand delivery broadened my smile. It also allowed me to add more complicated requests.

Still, I wondered if our pediatrician could shed light on Matthew's lack of speech. "Jackie, he said, "you're making a mountain out of a molehill. As a teacher, you're expecting Matthew to follow right with along with your textbook learning." That answer did not make any sense to me. I knew babies began contorting their mouths as if they wanted to talk well before they actually do. At age two, Matthew didn't even know how to begin.

Fortunately, Matthew was not frustrated by any of this and greeted each day happily. *So* happy that thoughts frequently passed through his little head, and he would begin to chuckle. "Richard," I'd giggle, "he just told himself another joke."

He was happy, and he was curious. As a toddler, Matthew loved playing with things – any things. Whatever toy he picked up, he studied it as if to ask, "How does this work? What does this do?" He was never interested in trucks or drawing. But Legos were ideal and provided hours of entertainment. So did sandboxes. He loved the feel of sand running through his hands.

What also interested him was our water heater. Well, to be clear, ours and everyone else's. Visiting anyone's home, his first request was, "May I please see your water heater?" To this day, we have no idea why. Neither does Matthew. When asked, he can only shake his head and laugh.

Matthew had another fascination – animals, all animals. Even from his stroller, he squeaked out excited, high-pitched noises while stretching out his little arm to touch any dog who passed. He didn't have to reach far; they gravitated to him. Matthew found similar joy in discovering insects. As a child, he somehow caught bees and held them oh-so-carefully by their wings. Captivated by the black stripe on their yellow body, he *had* to bring them to me to see.

Children in our neighborhood were keenly aware of his re-spect for animals. If a small garden snake was spotted in their yard, we heard the holler, "Mathhhewww!" Out he would rush, gesturing with his hands and shouting, "Away, Away." It was not that he feared for the neighbors' safety; he worried they would scare the poor snake.

When preschool rolled around, Matthew wanted to go for one reason only – to play with the things they had. Their toys, just like those at home, were more than just thingamajigs – they were to be investigated. He gave each a thorough exam, checking them up-side down and inside out. Each inspection could easily take sev-eral minutes. Perhaps this is why Matthew became inordinately hooked on shapes.

His father, an engineer who also loved shapes, bolstered this interest at home. One day, riding in the car, Matthew blurted out, "Catenary." I looked around but did not see a cat. "Catenary?" I questioned. "Catenary!" Matthew reiterated, pointing towards the sky. Richard leaned over to inform me that a *catenary* is the shape a wire forms between two posts.

It was not only animals, shapes, and water heaters that held Matthew's attention, he was also hooked on music. One of Richard's and my favorite records was the *Beach Boys Christmas Album*. As a toddler, Matthew would put his father's headphones on and lie down under the Christmas tree. We would see him looking up – mesmerized by the twinkling lights and calmed by the soothing harmonies.

Matthew was interested in so many things. In nursery school, he became fixated on numbers and could not learn them fast enough. We were thrilled imagining how well Matthew must be doing in school. That is – until his teacher informed us that while he eagerly participated in activities, he did not interact with other classmates. On some level, I knew this because if I asked if so-and-so was at school that day, he could not answer. Matthew's attention at school was exclusively on shapes and numbers.

His teacher's news was a concern, but we held out hope that Matthew would change. We already witnessed that when he outgrew his aversion to being touched. I knew, too, that Matthew could attach to people; I saw that with his father. Matthew adored Richard. I have pictures of the two of them on a Saturday morning at the kitchen table – Richard, reading the paper while Matthew sits blissfully on his lap. Most of the time, he followed Richard around like a duck. One day, I peered out the window, and, sure enough, he was trailing behind his father. But I had to look again when I saw that Matthew was walking with a limp. When that hobbling continued inside the house, I took him for X-rays. The doctor who examined Matthew told us that the pictures showed no abnormality and that his legs seemed fine. But he then turned to Richard, saying "I see that *you* have a limp." Matthew, it turns out, was imitating the man he loved, walking like the father he loved. We got to work and corrected that gait using marching music and walking imitation games.

Matthew missed Richard when he went to work. But the minute the front door opened at the end of the day, Matthew was jubilant, "Daddyfissit home!" Any problem Matthew had encountered that day he knew would be solved by "Daddyfissit." Matthew was bright; we saw that. Connections were happening all the time, but something was off, and we did not know what or why. That concern got tucked away; our second son, Andrew, arrived.

Now with two, our hands were full. Richard was always helpful. On Saturdays, the three of them headed to the nearby beach. He so wanted to be with them and they with him. One day, I suggested we take them to the Boston Common. While sitting on the grass enjoying the sunny day, a group of Hari Krishnas assembled nearby. As they began singing and swaying, their music grew louder. Matthew got so swept away clapping to the music that his stroller began rocking. *Thank God he's the age he is,* I thought, *because otherwise, we might have lost him.*

Richard was the fun part; then there was me. I could not help but worry about Matthew's speech. Finally, in 1976, I requested an evaluation at Children's Hospital. I also asked for a hearing test. He was just two and a half but had constant ear infections, and I wondered if those affected his speech. Doctors found nothing wrong with his ears, but they did find speech deficiencies. One neurologist who took me aside said, "I would question *autism*, but I don't know if that's what this is." (It was not until 1980 that The American Psychiatric Association's DSM-III manual established autism as a separate diagnosis.)

From my schooling, *I* knew what that was, and the word alone scared me to death. Just suggesting autism, I began stepping up our language exercises at home. We played word games, and I talked to Matthew using long, wordy sentences. I also gave him directions and tasks to do. In the evening, Matthew would be in the highchair, Andrew in his carrier seat. While I fed Matthew, I began: "Andrew is *on* the table,"

Then *I* climbed on the table and said, "Mommy is *on* the table. See Mommy? Mommy is *on* the table."

Then I would duck out of sight. "Mommy is *under* the table." I sang.

I'd poke back up, smile, and say, "Bye! Mommy's going *under* the table."

Silly as it might sound, that kind of play worked – those prepositions stuck.

We also read books to him, all sorts of books, all the time. When we asked Matthew to choose one, he always brought back *Caps for Sale*. With pure delight (and garbled words), he would read his favorite page over and over, his head bobbing along in sync.

"Look to de white,

Look to de lef.

Look Up,

Look don.

Noooo capz."

We were delighted that he was learning so fast and having fun, but we still knew he needed help. After their testing, staff at Children's Hospital directed Matthew to their Speech and Language room. Here he went with four or five other children three days a week for the next year and a half. (We parents watched on closed-circuit monitors.)

At first, Matthew raced into the room to secure his place – under the table. That remained *his* spot for some time until one day, he walked in, joined the group, and sat in a chair. From then on, he headed to the same chair and took out the same toy he had the day before. I was familiar with his burning need for things to remain the same and took note that it had continued here.

His teacher, Dorry Brown, was phenomenally skilled and incredibly observant. Once Matthew settled in, she mixed up the day's routine. Quickly Matthew interjected,

"No, No Dowee Bwown."

She answered quietly, "We're going to do it this way today, Matthew, but we'll do it the other way tomorrow."

Surprisingly, he agreed, as long as it went back to usual the next day!

Dorry had such a calm voice that Matthew would slowly lean in her direction and rest his head on her as she read aloud. He adored her, but he was also smitten by a cute little girl in the class. Every day he made sure she sat next to him. She, in turn, held his hand. I do not know why he zeroed in on her other than she was so pretty! It could also be that she was gentle, like Dorry. It did not matter. He had made a friend – his first friend – and I was there to see it.

Once settled in, Matthew got to work. After hours and hours of speech and language activities, his words began sounding right. These weekly sessions were hard work for both of us. One evening, particularly weary from another day at Children's, I sat at the kitchen table, put my head down, and started to cry. Suddenly, this little hand reached over from his highchair and patted my head. He did not know why mommy was crying; he did not have words or know what to do, but he got a feeling, and it said, "Mommy's sad." For the first time, I felt hopeful.

Matthew left Children's Hospital with improved fluency. But lingering speech issues still made it hard to understand him. Children's Hospital was not giving up. Dorry came out to observe Matthew in nursery school and assess the kindergarten class he was going to. She offered us advice and then suggested ways for teachers to help Matthew in that *other* area, the one we tucked away – his lack of social skills.

Dorry opened this door again. Where should we begin? We did notice that Matthew did not make eye contact. I had hoped he would outgrow it. But now, with Dorry's mention of delayed *social skills* and that *autism* word from the neurologist, I began to wonder.

But I could put it to the side because Matthew kept surprising us. I walked into his kindergarten's end-of-the-year performance and saw *my* son, front and center, at the piano bench. His little feet were dangling high above the floor. The production began with Matthew playing "America the Beautiful." I had no idea this was coming. It was flawless. It was unbelievable. Then I remembered those visits to my mother's house. Routinely, Matthew headed straight for the basement to first check her water heater. Then he sat at her rickety piano, and we would hear him play. Often, it was something we had just heard on the way over.

Given his kindergarten debut, I asked if he would like to take lessons. Matthew said, "Yes." I signed him up with a local teacher and acquired a piano from Richard's mother. Soon Matthew was performing in recitals, and after a few years, he was quite accomplished.

Matthew took the bus to school starting in kindergarten. He did not like it much, but he managed. By third grade, the noise from the older students and the commotion onboard became over-whelming. I had a decision to make. I could keep Matthew on the bus and risk him not enjoying school, or I could relent and allow him to ride his bike. I wanted Matthew to *love* school, not just like it. So, on the bike he jumped, every day, all year long – for the next ten years!

Schoolwork was not an issue, but Matthew's speech still was. I became convinced that he should have a better command of words. He didn't, so we started him in private speech therapy.

The elementary school principal that year wanted to convene a "team meeting" to talk about an "education plan" for Matthew. That was fine; we wanted him in their speech therapy. The team – several educators, therapists, and administrators – began talking. They had another classroom in mind for Matthew – one for students with special needs. And without much discussion, they slid a paper over to us saying, "You need to sign here." I looked at it cursorily, picked up the pen they set in front of Richard, and pushed both the paper and pen back to them. Calmly I said, "We will come back when you want to talk about the educational plan for Matthew *in* the classroom." We never heard any more about that separate class.

Teachers knew Matthew loved school and appreciated challenging him. Both at home and school, Matthew was the kind of child who, if you said, "Jump through the hoop," he would go, especially if he liked you.

Matthew was not seen the same way by fellow students. He was not *one of them.* So, they made fun of him – often. He was a loner and had speech issues. Sadly, taunting and teasing began even in kindergarten and persisted through high school. I brought this up at so many parent/teacher meetings and even went to the school to say it must stop. Nothing was ever done.

Schoolmates could not figure Matthew out, and that worked to his advantage. One minute they were teasing him ruthlessly saying, "He's odd;" the next, they shook their heads in awe, "Look at what he can do!" Encouraged now by his many talents and heartened by teachers' praises, the bullying appeared to roll off Matthew's back – until it didn't. In junior high, some were pushing him to the limit. I felt terrible. What was worse? I was at a loss as to how to approach it. But I asked if he would like to talk to someone. Again, Matthew said, "Yes."

Matthew never had to tell me about the shenanigans at school; I sensed it. Once home, he hopped off his bike, opened the door, and called out, "I'd like to go swimming." That request began happening more often. I did not pry but asked if he would like a pool membership. Matthew's answer? "Yes."

Water, I recalled, had always soothed him. He had nightmares as a child. They were hard to dispel. Together we would peer in all the closets to confirm there were no scary monkeys from the

Wizard of Oz. And when that didn't work, I would place him in a warm bath. Instantly he would calm down. Baths, therefore, happened often. While in the tub one day, Andrew came along. Right then and there, Andrew decided *he* wanted to be in the tub too. So, in he climbed wearing the shoes I had just bought him. Matthew immediately pointed and screeched, "No, No Andwoo." Two seconds later, still eyeing Andrew in those shoes, Matthew was struck by the funniness and burst into laughter.

Silliness amuses Matthew, but in his younger years, he did not laugh a lot. It was not a way for him to shake things off. But I was always on the lookout for activities to assuage his anxiety. For a few years, we had him in 4-H, where he loved working with the animals. The joy he shared with us week after week triggered two thoughts. First – we had a good size backyard, and second – our pediatrician had goats. I went quickly to his office to ask where to get them. His wife, my friend, was so excited about our project that she kindly offered us two of theirs, Sassafras and Licorice.

That night I informed Richard of *our* plan, and the next day we shared it with Matthew and Andrew. Overjoyed, the three of them hurried off to buy a shed. In no time, it was assembled and enclosed by a chain-link fence. Soon, the adorable goats arrived. Matthew, in particular, was in seventh heaven.

Since Sassafras and Licorice were only four months old, they needed formula three times a day. I would make the concoction in the morning and put it in large Perrier bottles we repurposed to feed them. Each morning, two young, eager boys waited on the porch alongside two young, hungry goats. All eight eyes staring at me through the kitchen window.

Andrew, as it turned out, was not keen on this feeding business. He would often quit early, saying, "It's getting too sloppy!" Matthew took charge and happily fed both goats simultaneously. Sassafras, who finished first, would then target Licorice's meal.

But Matthew held firm, "No Sassafras you've had yours. This is hers." He was equitable with everything, including goats.

One summer day, I handed the boys their bottles and headed upstairs to make beds. Soon a high-pitched plea came from the bottom of the stairs, "Mom, can you come down here?!" There, in the living room, was Sassafras standing at a side table devouring our houseplant. Like bulls in a china shop, Licorice and Sassafras were bumping into everything. And along the way, they were expelling "presents" *everywhere*. Matthew and Andrew, who let them in, were ordered to get them out. They were further directed to pick up all the little droppings. We never saw "Sassy" or "Lulu" in the house again.

Life moved along. With the help of swimming, talk therapy, and goats, Matthew found a bit of solace. Around the age of ten, entering junior high, I asked, "Would you like to try another instrument?" "Yes," he said and, without a minute's hesitation, declared, "the trumpet." Like the piano, Matthew picked the trumpet up quickly. He joined the school band and, for years, played in the town's annual Memorial Day parade. Matthew stayed with it for all four high school years. (To this day, Matthew plays in marching bands in several New England parades.)

Music lifted him, as did most of his classes. Latin was introduced in seventh grade, and it clicked. Like his preschool affinity for shapes and numbers, Matthew could not get enough Latin. I even gave him a joke book in Latin for Christmas. That day, after all the gifts were open, I began preparing our holiday dinner only to discover I had run out of butter. With some urgency, I asked Matthew if he would scoot up to the convenience store for some. When he did not come back, I began pacing. Finally, he came through the door. "Matthew," I pleaded, "*where* have you been?" He handed me the butter saying, "Reading the jokes in the car. They're good!"

Matthew studied hard. We saw that. At the end of eighth grade, Matthew was inducted into the Junior National Honor Society. The day that notification came, I remarked to Richard, "And this is the one they wanted to put into a special ed class? The best thing we ever did was to put that pen down."

There was nothing the matter with Matthew's brain. But there were these usual societal norms that eluded Matthew. One night, not long after Richard had a hip replaced, the four of us went out to dinner. We parked and followed the walkway into the restaurant. Suddenly, Richard tripped, falling face down. Andrew and I rushed to his aid. Matthew walked right by him. I was shocked, even angry. Later I asked what he was thinking. He could not explain it, but I figured out that Matthew truthfully did not know what to do. Step by step, I had to explain the protocol people usually follow. I must have driven the point home; for weeks afterward, he asked anyone who even stumbled if he could help them. Matthew is better now when he sees someone fall, but he misses other cues and can be puzzled in social situations.

Matthew took Latin through tenth grade. When he was told that he needed a second language, he chose Spanish and began to study it over the summer. After taking a placement test that fall, Matthew was able to bypass Spanish 1 and enter Spanish 2. While he did well in it, he never lost his love of Latin. So enamored, he took one of his college achievement tests in Latin and, yes, scored well.

Math, however, remained Matthew's first love and his strongest suit. What was not his strong suit was standing up to bullies. Often Matthew had to hurry to get to his next class. It meant rushing up a set of stairs only to be met at the top by the same student who stood there waiting, always sniggering. Once Matthew reached the landing, this bully took all his books and threw them back down the two flights. Daunted, Matthew would head back down to pick them up. It happened repeatedly.

Somehow, I got wind of it. Naturally, I was steaming, but I struggled to figure out what my involvement should be. Richard, too, was at a loss. We knew that we did not want this intimidation to get to the point where Matthew would not want to go to school.

I had to broach the subject.

"Matthew, there's one way to deal with people like this. Words don't stop bullies. Sometimes you have to take the upper hand. Would you feel comfortable pushing him back?"

Matthew immediately spoke up. "I might get into trouble."

"No," I answered firmly, "I'll make sure you don't!"

The next time Matthew saw this student waiting, the plan kicked in. When he reached the landing, *he* grabbed the bully's books. The student lost his footing and tumbled – right down the stairs. Matthew walked on. That afternoon he told us that he got detention. No! Into the principal's office I hurried. I knew this rascal had probably embellished the story to look like *he* was the innocent one.

"Look," I said, "this student has been bullying our son for years! I've talked to staff here about it several times, and nothing has changed. We gave our son permission to do whatever he had to do to stop it. Yes, he did it. And he's *not* getting detention. This kid asked for it. And more!" Because of Matthew's unsullied record, detention was dismissed. And better still, an empowered Matthew emerged.

The bullying ended, the teasing did not. But because Matthew is the kind of person he is, several classmates stood behind him. So did his brother. One day, Andrew happened to run into someone who had perpetrated an incident against Matthew. He wasted no time chit-chatting. He punched him, nearly breaking his jaw. Andrew finished by saying, "If you bother my brother again, I'll be back!"

Matthew was our definition of resilience. Counseling, swimming, and his goats helped steady him, but it was his endless curiosity that seemed to keep his despair at bay. One afternoon, out of the blue, he began talking about dancing. I was intrigued. *Did this fascination come from seeing the movie American Graffiti?* My intuition kicked in – *maybe he does not quite know what to do with this interest.* "Matthew," I queried, "would you like to take lessons?" Surprised by the question, he tilted his head as if thinking, *"Oh, is this what the next step should be?"* Not another second passed; Matthew said, "Yes." For the next three years, Matthew took the arm of many teachers at Arthur Murray Dance Studio. He became so adept at ballroom dancing he was soon asked to compete.

Dancing transformed Matthew. It connected him to others in ways we could never have planned. It also disconnected any lingering aversion he had to being touched. The smoother he got as a dancer, the more self-confident he became. Anyone sitting alone – be forewarned; he will ask you to dance the minute the music begins.

In many ways, Matthew was blossoming. But one habit of his concerned me. Unbeknownst to me, Matthew had a routine while riding his bike to school each day. He would pass the convenience store in the morning and pick up a Coke to drink on his way. He made the same stop on the way home. When I learned how long this had been going on, I spoke up emphatically, "Matthew, this Coke is killing you! You have got to stop!" He dug in. It was not going to happen. This was the only thing I ever asked Matthew to do that he answered with a very grown-up, "No."

But Matthew rarely said "No" to Andrew. He adored his brother and wanted nothing more than to be just like him – popular, athletic, and clever. Sure, Andrew looked after Matthew, but Andrew wanted to have some fun too. He would instigate plans, not all of which were aboveboard. The two were a bit like Mutt and Jeff, but I called them *Mis* and *Hap*. At age fourteen, Andrew convinced Matthew, then sixteen, to drive him and his rowboat to the beach. The problem was that neither had a license. Astutely, Matthew spoke up about this snag. Andrew reasoned with him, saying, "It's okay. You already took driving lessons." Matthew decided that made sense, so he helped load the boat onto the car, and off they went. Matthew returned just as Richard and I pulled into the driveway. So great was Matthew's shock we could not punish him. I had to walk away to hide my laughter. *Mis* and *Hap* were at it again!

Matthew enjoyed helping his brother. He also liked to keep busy. Friday afternoons, he would burst in from school asking for money. Not for candy or soda but for rug cleaner. Yup, Matthew cleaned his rug (and his room) thoroughly every Friday. I was always a bit puzzled.

He did not get paid for doing that, but he did get a paycheck working as a bagger at our local grocery store. He enjoyed it despite being yelled at by a customer for putting the milk on top of her grapes. It embarrassed him terribly. But the boss, bless his heart, smoothed it over, saying, "Don't worry, she yells at everyone."

Matthew's favorite job in high school was working with a local CVS pharmacist as a tech assistant. Customers approached the counter with prescriptions for themselves and sometimes for their sick or injured animals. Matthew made sure he had something to do with those! "How is Maggie today," he'd greet a customer, "Is she feeling better?" "How is that rash on Clem's left leg?" His interest was sincere; he hung on their every word. Matthew would remember Clem today and probably ask if his left leg has healed.

Matthew had a unique way of interacting with people. As a toddler, he had to get to know you before you could pick him up. Growing up, he was usually the quiet one, but would sometimes make conversations with adults who shared similar interests. In high school, Matthew became involved in different groups, but he was always alone, on the periphery. Matthew even preferred going on a vacation alone. Once, having saved his money, he set out to explore amusement parks. Matthew would travel to one, ride every ride, look for the animal exhibits, and move on to the next park. After a week, home he came, animated and eager to show us his many pictures: rides and animals; rides and animals; and more rides and animals. We were glad he had such a good time.

Matthew graduated from high school and was inducted into the National Honor Society after being on the honor roll all four years. He went on to Goucher College to major in math and music. Matthew wanted a city college with a campus. What he liked more was that Goucher was a train ride away from DC's Kennedy Center. The Center's music drew him in often, but it was their Christmas tree that held special appeal. He went in several times each year just to gaze at it and would call immediately, "Mom, you wouldn't believe the lights, they're beautiful!"

I was nervous enough knowing college was so brand-new to him. I worried. He was not around the corner if something went wrong. Nothing terrible ever happened, and Goucher turned out to be a perfect fit. It was small enough, and it had a certain intimacy we *all* came to appreciate. When Matthew left in September, Sassafras had developed a lump on his head. We assured him that we would take Sassy to the vet. None of us wanted bad news. But, when the worst came, the vet told us the humane thing to do.

How would Matthew take this? I wondered. I knew I could be an anchor at the end of the phone here, but what about there? Somehow, I got the idea to call the college chaplain. A wonderful man answered the phone, and I explained that I was Matthew's mother.

"I wonder if I could ask you for help?"

"Of course," he answered.

"Matthew has a pet goat whose name is Sassafras, and Sassafras is very sick."

There was quite a bit of silence on the other end of the phone.

"Now tell me again who it is?"

"Sassafras."

"And he is?"

"He's a goat."

This had to be a first for this poor chaplain.

I continued, "Matthew has cared for this goat for ten years. He left for Goucher, knowing Sassafras had a lump on his head. We learned that the prognosis is not good. We won't put him down until Matthew comes home for Thanksgiving. But I want someone there to know about this in case he comes back upset."

When Matthew arrived home, Richard and the two boys dug a grave. The vet came, administered a single shot, and gently laid Sassafras in the ground. Matthew seemed fine. However, we never thought about the impact this might have on poor Licorice. Watching all of this from her pen, she instinctively fled and for a long time, kept us at arm's length.

When Matthew returned to college, the chaplain called him. "I know about your goat. How did things go? Would you like to come and talk with me?"

Matthew said, "Yes."

After their conversation, Matthew began attending the chaplain's Sunday services. I got a call.

"Mom," he began, "they serve wine and call it the blood of Christ. Did you know that?"

"It's a ritual in some religions," I explained, "and yes, you haven't heard it before. It's perfectly okay to drink the wine if that's what you'd like to do."

"Well, they have bread too!"

"Good, have the bread and the wine. If you don't want all the wine, you can just dip your bread into it. You don't have to have it at all if that's what you decide."

Once Matthew understood the conundrum of the blood and wine, he and this kind chaplain developed a special friendship. It lasted all four years.

College allowed Matthew to explore. One night, walking across campus, he heard the familiar sound of sixties music in the distance. Matthew followed it and came upon a practicing dance troupe – Goucher's dance majors, he learned. Captivated, he showed up each week to watch them. The professor soon asked, "Matthew, would you like to join us?" "Yes," he replied. Lo and behold Matthew not only picked up their dance moves, but he also traveled with them and danced in their shows. (Matthew kept in touch with many teachers; this one until her death in 2020.)

One of his performances was a dance and music show spanning the forties to the fifties. I invited a favorite aunt and her daughter to join me. And what a show it was! Matthew's Arthur Murray talents had ratcheted up a few notches. We discovered that night that Matthew had become an extraordinary, all-around dancer.

I was thrilled knowing Matthew was happy, but I had concerns about his future. What was it going to look like? In his sophomore year, I posed a question. "Matthew, would you do one more thing for us? We'd like you to see a doctor who will do a few tests. We want to get another person's point of view as to how you're doing." Matthew said, "Yes."

The doctor's findings came after Matthew returned to Goucher. "This is classic Asperger's," he reported. Richard and I had never even heard of Asperger's and had no clue what it meant. (Asperger's was first described by Hans Asperger in 1944. Asperger's syndrome wasn't used as a diagnosis until 1994.)

Coincidently, just after this test, Andrew asked, "Mom what's really wrong with Matthew?" It was the first time Andrew ever hinted at this question. "I don't know if something is *wrong* with him," I replied, "but we just learned that Matthew has Asperger's syndrome. I don't know much about it, but all the things we see with him that seem odd and different? They're related to this Asperger's syndrome. Certain wires just aren't quite complete. But the ones that are? They are solid!"

Andrew stopped at Barnes & Noble that day and bought a

book on Asperger's syndrome. It helped him put all the pieces together. And the respect for his brother only deepened. Matthew, he saw, was and is a competent and genuine human being.

After graduating from Goucher, Matthew was eager to teach and sent out applications. He landed a job at Shaw's headquarters while waiting to hear back from high schools. But what he really hankered after was a place of his own. Matthew found his dream apartment with plenty of neighborhood animals to befriend. One fluffy fella from somewhere down the street waited on his porch every day for him to come home.

After a year at Shaw's, a teaching job opened, and Matthew took it. However, it was in a rough-and-tumble town. So rough that police entered his classroom one day and took out a student who was party to a serious crime. We did not say anything for a while. But when he called saying he would be working late, I knew he would be the only one in the building and would not leave until it was dark. I finally spoke up. "I don't feel comfortable with you doing that, Matthew. What do you think about looking for another job?" Matthew said, "Yes."

Change is hard, but this one came with a silver lining. Matthew realized that the classroom was not for him; it was too confusing. The curriculum also confined him. He enjoyed teaching math to those who wanted to learn it and loved finding people as passionate about it as he was. So, he began a tutoring business, and as it grew, he completed a master's degree in Math and Secondary Education.

Matthew stuck with whatever he set out to accomplish. So, we paid attention when he told us about his new interest. Matthew had decided to attend *Singles* events. There was dancing at these affairs; we knew that was good for him. He then mentioned dating. And soon, the name Maryellen was coming up often. Finally, he introduced us, and Richard and I breathed a sigh of relief. Such a great choice! Such a fabulous fit! All my adult life, I prayed that my boys would find someone who loved them as much as we did. She does! Matthew and Maryellen married a year later in 2009.

Now thirty-five, with a new bride and a master's degree, Matthew thought he would try teaching at the junior college level but he learned that they wanted someone with a Ph.D. So, he began that coursework – all while carrying a busy tutoring caseload in several school systems. Life was more than full.

After two years of this grueling schedule, he met with his post-graduate advisor. She warned him of the steep incline ahead and suggested he focus solely on his Ph.D. That meeting came just after he and Maryellen decided to adopt a baby. They knew this process would demand time and patience. Now at crossroads, Matthew chose to forego his Ph.D. and begin a family with Maryellen. They adopted a newborn they named Henry Richard. Joy fills their home. *What a journey,* I thought, *considering the challenges Matthew has met to where he is today: a father with a CAGS (a post-master's degree), a wife, and a family.*

Matthew is a great father. He is attentive and exceedingly patient. Maryellen's love of children has always been apparent. She has spent years running nursery school and daycare programs. But, having a child changes everything. Life moves at a quicker pace, and new demands come from all directions.

I wondered how Matthew would manage. It didn't take long to notice how a new family with a caring wife can help someone change. Henry has awakened Matthew. He can pull from Matthew skills we would not have known *how* to teach. Matthew can now juggle more than one thing at a time. He can also consider different ways to look at a situation. Approaching life with less rigidity means he lives with less stress.

Maryellen continues to introduce Matthew to new ways of being in the world. She loves when friends and family visit and encourages them to do so often. She also enjoys throwing parties just as much as going to them. This is a considerable shift for

Matthew, one he seems to welcome. However, there still are gaps in his comprehension. Last year, Matthew began organizing a surprise party for Maryellen's birthday. He had never thrown a party. We learned of it second hand and wondered why we hadn't heard anything about it from Mathew. I asked when he called one day. He answered with a flurry of rushed sentences that did not give a clear answer. That was familiar to me. It meant he was confused and did not know *how* to respond.

It is now forty-six years later. I continue to have certain expectations knowing how we raised Matthew. I can still get angry. While he appears to be so bright and caring, I have to remember the night he walked by his father sprawled out on the sidewalk. What can appear as self-absorption sometimes is not that. Norms, mores, habits – even common sense in certain areas – have not stuck and maybe never will.

But that's Matthew. That's Autism. And that's Asperger's.

A short time ago, in the late afternoon of June 2nd, a tragedy struck our family. Andrew was taken from our life. The cause? A hidden heart disease. Abruptly, our three worlds stopped. It was as if a main support of a house fell. We were left hoping the structure would still stand. At first, Matthew had no words. He did not know what to do with his suffering, but his sorrow over losing his best friend was palpable. Matthew wanted to attend grief counseling with Richard and me. Months later, he went on to individual therapy and was urged to talk even more about feelings. It has brought him to new levels of understanding.

The three of us often reflect on the "new normal;" it is still hard. I never, ever thought I would lose a child. Then again, I never thought I would give birth to a child with special needs. Recently Matthew said to me, "I used to think that when you and Dad got older, I would always have Andrew to help me do what is needed to help you."

Matthew is an older, gentler version of the kind-hearted,

young boy. He still cannot live without music, an animal for a companion, or playing math games with his father. And dancing? He and Maryellen share this passion and are a fabulous couple to watch!

Matthew has so much to share, but he is quiet. And because others do not know *how* to engage, they often don't. His autism has had its challenges, but through him, Richard and I have learned new ways of seeing the world. Something would have been missing in our lives if opportunities for him had been cut short. His mix of distinctions and differences is what makes Matthew, Matthew. We would not want it any differently.

Millie and Bobby

18 Months

6 Years Old

40 Years old

41 Years old

Dawn and Sean

15 Months

8 Years old

15 Years old

22 Years old

Dawn and Jenna

15 Months

5 Years old

7 Years old

13 Years old

Jackie and Matthew

Matthew (L) age 5

10 Years old

21 Years old

43 Years old

Janine and Patrick

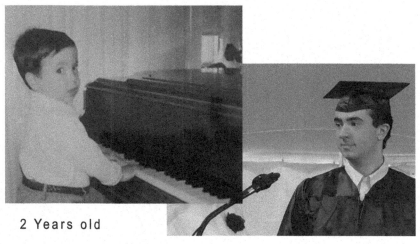

2 Years old

21 Years old

25 Years old

25 Years old

Betsy and Merriweather

7 Years old

8 Years old

17 Years old

18 Years old

Danielle and Johnny

7 Years old

7 Years old

10 Years old

Johnny 10, Bella 8

Danielle and Bella

7 Years old

7 Years old

8 Years old

Johnny age 10 and
Bella age 8

Janine and Patrick

Pervasive Developmental Disorder – Not Otherwise Specified (PDD-NOS)

Determined to connect with my son, I spent years trying to *fix* his autism. Finally, I stopped and fell back into being completely in love with the magic of everything Patrick.

It's now, some years later, that I regret not paying closer attention to his small victories early on. Fear and worry about his future robbed me of the present.

When Patrick was young, I did not want anyone telling me about their son's life in high school or even elementary school. I couldn't think about it. A speech therapist saw how sad I was and pleaded with me to go to the high school graduation of a young man with autism just to see how he turned out. She offered me hope, but hope was a long way off for someone immersed in the life of a loved one with disabilities.

We did not plan to have children when Scott and I married in 1990. We thought the world was too scary a place, and we were not cut out for that challenge. But unexpectedly, three years later, I was pregnant and Scott was all in. He was so determined to do this right that he bought a book called, *How to Have a Smarter Baby*. We followed each suggestion to the *T*. Every day for the next nine months, we played Bach, Beethoven, and Brahms to our baby in utero. Step one, they said, in assuring our son's intelligence.

Patrick's birth was somewhat traumatic. Three times the umbilical cord wrapped around his head, and his heart rate fluctuated considerably. Fortunately, at 7 lbs., 6 oz., he was declared healthy. However, Patrick was a colicky baby and suffered tormenting GI issues. His screaming was intense. I would spend all night trying to calm him and his aching stomach. Patrick had numerous ear infections and was saturated with antibiotics. Then, at ten months, Patrick contracted a severe case of chicken pox. The itching was merciless – his fragility real.

But there was something more. While Patrick was active enough, he seemed far away. He also was not affectionate. Baths, which were calming and could last for hours, were the one occasion that offered a small window to connect with him.

Since there was always something going on, our pediatrician saw us almost weekly. I pleaded with him, asking, "What is contributing to this barrage of illnesses, his sleeplessness, and his crying?" He did not seem concerned.

When Patrick was a year old, I brought this doctor a different concern after reading yet another book, *What to Expect the First Year*. It stated, "they should have a dozen words in their repertoire." Patrick was a far cry from that. I was heartbroken but wanted to believe my pediatrician who was telling me, "Not to worry, boys don't develop language 'til fiveish." Having dismissed my concerns one too many times, I asked for Patrick's records and moved to a woman pediatrician who listened supportively.

Aside from Patrick's physical and maturational challenges, other behaviors seemed odd. For one, Patrick was satisfied living in his swing, one that I was forever winding up. I saw that same idle contentment on the playground. Others his age were busy in the world around them – running about, pointing to birds, and screeching with delight. Patrick showed no interest in any of it. He was in his world. I knew something was up but did not want to say anything. Scott would not want to hear it and would disagree.

It was easier to turn a blind eye when I remembered that Patrick had passions. As a toddler, he loved putting together a giant floor puzzle of the alphabet. He would rummage through a heap of letters, pull out an *A*, run across the room, place it face up, zoom back, sort through the pile again and pull out a *B*. In no time, the alphabet was complete. And I watched as he did it again and again, all day. I tried telling myself, "he's just enthusiastic." Yet, I quietly wondered how he could know all the letters and still not speak.

Besides recognizing letters, Patrick was also counting. He emptied his cup of numbers onto his highchair's tray and lined them up from one to ten. Then he would look for another *one* to make eleven, move on to twelve, and so on. Scott began to think, "he's a genius! After all, Einstein didn't talk 'til later." I tried clinging to that. Yet, the day came when every time Patrick went for that cup of numbers, I felt my stomach turn. I did not want him to put them in order one more time. I knew it did not mean he was a genius; it was a strange busyness. Again, I was reluctant to bring it up. So, I lived with worry.

The focus for us turned to his language. I so wanted him to have those twelve words. We decided that he would learn words through books. Patrick loved books! So, Scott and I dug in and read him piles of Dr. Seuss stories. Soon we noticed that Patrick could pick out random words like "Pop." There was no comprehension, just decoding, and he was a quick study. All this before the age of two. I had hope again!

Around this time, I went to Philadelphia to visit family. I spent a day with my brother's wife, Theresa, and their child, Patrick's age. Patrick began doing the number thing, and somehow, I let my secret out. "Do you think this is different?" I asked. She had the guts to answer, "I'm a nurse, not a doctor, but, yes, I would get it checked out." Naturally, I did not want to hear this. But I knew that sooner or later, someone was going to say it. How long was I going to live in this state of fear and denial? Something had to break.

To this day, I thank God for Theresa. After that visit, I was back at my pediatrician's office, in tears begging for tests. For what? I didn't know. "Okay," she said, "let's first get him a hearing test, and then we will send him to Boston for a developmental evaluation. But I want to tell you that they will be looking for effects and behaviors resembling hermits – you know, those antisocial people?" That description scarred me for life. I thought back to a story my father told me of an odd uncle who lived under the stairs. I felt like I was falling off a cliff.

She continued. "We're looking for something called Pervasive Developmental Disorder (PDD); it's *autism*." I flashed back to a day in the late 1980s when, in college, I read a chapter for a psychology class on the subject. It described a boy, lost in himself, twirling away in a corner. The horror of that image never left me. Now, here I was, staring down that barrel.

Patrick's diagnosis of PDD came the day of the tests. It was 1996; he was two. I was numb. We did not plan on this; after all, we read the darn books! Their assessment also confirmed his limited language. Patrick spoke just five words. One was "Buzz." Not "Mom" or "Dad" but "Buzz," the main character of yet another Disney movie. Patrick fixated on those movies. Even as a toddler, he figured out how to stop, rewind and resume movies on our VCR like a pro. It went on all day – stop, rewind, play; stop, rewind, play – the same scene over and over. While the constant repetition drove *me* crazy, it brought him peace. Most days, I was too overwhelmed by it all to think about it.

After the diagnosis from Children's Hospital, Patrick was placed in "Early Intervention," a supportive pre-school environment. There he was immersed not only in physical and occupational therapies but music therapy as well. I dragged myself to all his sessions despite being worn down. I so wanted Patrick to talk, and I yearned for Scott to accept his diagnosis.

I became one of those vocal moms, desperate for these therapies to fix what I was seeing. I got a glimmer of hope one day. Michelle, his music therapist, suggested I come in to watch Patrick. I had to be discreet, she warned, or he would not perform. Michelle started the class dancing with wooden farm animals in her hands. Next, holding just a pig, she began singing and beating lightly on a drum. I looked over at Patrick. The rhythm captivated him.

"Pig wants to dance." She sang, slowly.

"Pig wants to dance.

Dance, Pig. Dance...."

She paused, and faintly, I heard Patrick peep, "Pig."

His first words. He sang them! I was stunned – and nearly in tears.

I burst through the door with the news. "Patrick sang his first words!" Music, we now knew, was our road to his language, and Michelle was going to be our guide. She had gained Patrick's trust and, by doing so, allowed him to show her the way. When Michelle pulled out the guitar, he wanted to strum with her. If she went to the piano, he wanted to play too. Music was coming quickly, words slowly.

Scott, too, found hope. He thought that *his* love of music had trickled into his son and that Patrick, like him, was a budding musician. So sure, Scott ran out to buy him a keyboard. He then labeled each key with its correlating note. Patrick's letter recognition skills, thought Scott, would help him learn to read notes.

Patrick spent hours at the keyboard reading the letter and tapping the key. Then he added keys and began making melodies. One evening, Scott and I got a startle. We snuck around a corner to see *Fantasia* playing on the TV and Patrick at his keyboard. We heard Beethoven's Fifth Symphony and looked at each other in disbelief. "It almost sounds like Patrick's playing it." And he was.

Patrick never did master reading music; he didn't have to. Through hours of repetition came his gift of playing music by ear. Patrick can listen to a song, pick out a series of notes, and play them in his brain as he heads to play them on a piano. Could he have been studying all this listening to classical music in utero?

We always had music on in our house, but now I added singing to Patrick's bath time. One day, I wrapped him in a towel, laid him on the bed, and began with a calming Disney refrain,

"No matter how your heart is grieving,

If you keep on believing

The dreams that you wish

Will come ..."

Softly he sang out, "TRUE."

For the first time, I found a way *into* him – and he to me. My innermost wish was granted; it came through Disney.

While I now had a way to relate to Patrick, I was losing a way to relate to my husband. Scott disagreed with Patrick's diagnosis of autism; I needed support to face it.

Some encouragement came from moms along the way, but now I wanted to form a formal parent support group, so I did. I did not have to look far. The mid-to-late nineties saw an enormous surge in the number of children diagnosed with autism. The statistics then and now are alarming. When Patrick was born in 1994, one in ten thousand children were labeled autistic. When Patrick was diagnosed two years later, it was one in a thousand; and by the end of the decade, it was one in 150. Today, in 2020, figures show that one in fifty-four children have autism.

Parents came in droves, looking to me for help and direction. The schools were not giving it, nor were our communities. We needed to do something!

I rented a hall, hired babysitters to watch our children, began active discussions, and shared the slew of books I had garnered. I also learned of parents in surrounding towns who were equally eager to break new ground for this population. Together with educational advocates and teachers, we started "The Autism Center of the South Shore." We were a determined bunch and quickly received nonprofit status. The Center continued to grow, and schools began to take notice.

One major accomplishment was establishing the first social groups for people with autism on the South Shore. We ran countless benefits to pay for those and other services. But after five years of rigorous work and little funding, on top of the growing needs of our children and families, energies were depleted. The Center sadly closed but a new door opened for me.

Patrick's pre-K teacher saw that I was an involved parent and learned I was in between jobs. She mentioned that Quincy schools were expanding their special needs program and suggested I apply for a position. I was hired as an intensive special needs tutor and then became a speech therapy assistant. I loved my work and my fellow workers. The help they gave Patrick and their dedication inspired me to pay it forward. Knowing how critical the early years are for those on the spectrum, I decided to help parents with limited English understand how to apply at home what was taking place in the classroom. My days were full and fulfilling.

Patrick's little head was also bursting with interests. There were numbers and letters and dozens of movies and songs rolling through. Then there was reading and the keyboard to master. A myriad of seeds was germinating, just waiting to be watered.

Quincy had started a "substantially separate" autism program for three- to five-year-olds. In its second year, Patrick joined their class of seven. Its focus was on "total communication." They used signing, as well as the customary verbal prompts and pictures. Patrick had begun to speak but now had picture boards to communicate. For a long time, this simplified things. We would say, "I want," and he could simply point to a picture on his board.

At least we were communicating, but it was his vocabulary we wanted to build. To that effort, we labeled everything in sight. We knew he could decode what was written – now we insisted he say it. The process was incredibly systematic. He would learn words, and we could perfect their clarity and flow. In my mind, if he was intelligible and sounded "normal," everything was going to be okay.

My goals were one thing. I did not know Patrick had plans of his own. As it turns out, he was exploring words too, looking for some to express his emotions – anger for one. When he did not get his way at home or in public, he suddenly began crying out in a loud, angry voice, "MIYAAAAA, MIYAAAAAAAAAA." Patrick was engrossed in the newly released movie, *The Lion King*. It was not until we watched the scene together where Mufasa is killed that I understood. Simba's thunderous roar, "Murderer," was Patrick's "MIYAAA." The scene sizzles: Patrick felt the rage and clung to "MIYAAA," to express his fury. My little three-year-old son mystified me. He understood so much. Yet, there were many contradictions.

By the late 1990s in the US, the autism "epidemic" was full-blown. Therapies touting a "cure" for autism began to flourish. Patrick had already been immersed in the *usual* ones: occupational therapy for sensory integration problems, physical therapy to correct his toe walking, and of course, speech therapy. Now eagerly, I delved into alternative treatments. One of them was Audio Integration Training (AIT Therapy.) Twice a day for two weeks, we drove a half-hour away for Patrick to don headphones and listen to music with filtered and modulated frequencies flowing in and out. The theory behind AIT is that by retraining the auditory system to normalize how the brain processes information, it's possible to reduce or even eliminate many signs of autism. People, they asserted, would speak more clearly and accurately. Their behavior, mood, and their social skills would also improve. Just what I was after!

Patrick had noticeable problems all along. His speech was indecipherable, his attention span was short, and he was very much in his world. We could pull him out with a song or a book, but otherwise, he would spend his days running around, talking to himself, and "stimming." But after a few of these AIT sessions, a near miracle happened. Patrick walked into the house, went straight to Scott, and hugged him. Coincidence? It was his first unprompted hug! Remarkable results continued. Patrick became more engaged with others and more connected.

Trying to fix his autism did not stop there. We took part in a controversial treatment called "Secretin Therapy." Secretin, a gastrointestinal hormone, is believed to function as a neurotransmitter and thought to be an effective intervention for warding off symptoms of autism. It is based on the idea that stomach issues, common among children with autism, can interfere with their ability to focus, which, in turn, impedes language development. They believed that once digestion problems are managed, one is "freed up" to move ahead with language acquisition skills. Being injected with a pig hormone was experimental. It was so suspect that they told us to enter the doctor's office through the back door. This, I realized, is the decision of a desperate mother!

Tied to Secretin Therapy was LGS, "Leaky Gut Syndrome." I took Patrick to Massachusetts General Hospital to explore it. When a specialist told me that it would require a biopsy and most likely surgery, I drew the line and said, "No."

I also took a local neurologist's suggestion on my mission to find a solution – a vitamin therapy called *Super New-Thera*. Biomedical approaches were popular at the time; many made sense to me. Patrick took this horrendous smelling liquid willingly, every day for a year. It would help with what autism "experts" concluded were vitamin deficiencies.

Vitamin deficiencies, attention deficits, gut issues, all of it! I was angry and wanted it to go away. One physical therapist finally turned to me, saying, "I do not know what you are trying to do. But sooner or later, you are going to have to realize he is who he is. Just accept it!" I might have been radical in my approach, but I am glad I did not accept things as they were.

Everything I tried had benefits, but I was careful not to discuss the roads we traveled with many people. They would have looked at me sideways. Periodically, Patrick and I would bump into someone and hear, "Wow, Patrick is doing great!" That feedback was all the assurance I needed.

I became more convinced that we could beat this autism. The next step was to pull Patrick out of "substantially separate" programs. I began researching. Norwell, I learned, was one of the few towns billing themselves as "inclusive." So, we moved. Patrick, now five, entered their integrative preschool program. That decision was to change the course of his life.

Norwell had a handful of others with special needs enrolled at the time. They wanted to do this right, and they set the bar high. They also listened to us, the parents. I insisted on an all-day program since he had come out of one. Happily, they put a comprehensive, full-day plan together and added customized therapies to fill lag times. Patrick thrived.

With the help of an academic aide and many supports, Patrick continued through the entire Norwell school system in regular classes. He followed classmates, was attentive to his work, and appeared to keep up with his peers. We discovered that he had an affinity for Spanish and excelled in Spanish honors classes throughout high school.

Some students may have made fun of Patrick, but for the most part, people, especially the girls, were kind to him. They also included him, which turned his earlier years as a loner around. The drama club welcomed him despite having a reputation for being quite exclusive. Patrick loved being a part of it. Sports teams also asked him to be the water guy. That forced something that was not right for him, but he enjoyed the social part of it. Knowing his varied music skills, the school asked him to start each basketball game by singing the national anthem.

Patrick felt most comfortable in the school's jazz band. He was a natural. And the more skilled Patrick became, the more the music teacher agreed he should try Berklee College of Music's summer program. We leapt at the opportunity. After his senior year, five days a week for eight weeks, Patrick ventured into Boston for a true college experience. His course load – six classes – was equivalent to a full semester. He managed the schedule, mastered moving between buildings, and completed the courses' expectations with enthusiasm. But, even with support, we saw it was a lot. Just traveling into Boston and navigating the busy streets to Mass Ave. was nerve-wracking. (Patrick's head was forever buried in his phone's GPS.) The course content was demanding, and the social piece – hanging out with fellow musicians – was challenging. Yet, he was holding his own and far from frazzled. We were, however.

Professors willingly altered their teaching styles. They were excited by him, and their feedback was encouraging. They commented on his overall demeanor, his hard work, and his skill level. So enamored of him, one professor remarked, "Patrick grew me."

We learned, however, that if Patrick were to continue at Berklee, his course load would be demanding, and all his classes would have to be tweaked. The conclusion was that Berklee would be a stretch for everyone, so we continued with plans already made for the fall.

Patrick had taken the state's MCAS test and passed, despite an "NI" (needs improvement) in math. On paper, his grades resembled others on a college track. However, I knew he needed training in independence skills and exposure to the vocational world. We found a three-year program at the Riverview School in Sandwich that did just that. Their "Grow Program" offered social skills training as well as classes in cooking, laundry, time management, and money – all structured to prepare students to live on their own.

That September, while unloading the car and settling Patrick in his dorm, I happened to glance over as he was eyeing his new surroundings. You can not quite put your finger on what is going on with the students there. Many are truly extraordinary, but many, too, are quirky. With his diverse skills and gentle ways, Patrick stood out, but he also belonged.

I watched as he drew a deep breath in and let go an audible sigh. I could almost hear, "Ahh, I can be me!" Initially, I was taken aback and immediately questioned if inclusion had been a mistake. I shook that thought off, realizing this was what we did for him. It was *his* journey. Norwell's schools had brought him to his full potential. And now, at Riverview, the trajectory of Patrick's life was about to fall into place.

He made friends, lots of them. One was Owen Suskind. They were drawn to each other because Owen, like Patrick, was fixated on Disney movies. Both had memorized dozens of them. Owen's parents, Ron and Cornelia, worried about this obsession just as we did. Worrying was bringing the Suskinds to their wits end. They had already faced one tragedy. Abruptly, at the age of three, Owen stopped talking.

Ron had tried to sever Disney from Owen's life but finally decided to change course. And that is when the miracle happened. Ron, Cornelia, and Disney brought language back to their son. One night, Ron crept into Owen's room, put on one of his Disney puppets, and, reaching the *puppeted* arm up onto Owen's bed, uttered a line from a Disney script. Owen quickly glanced over and instantly recited the next line.

Ron and Cornelia kept at it. They reenacted parts of movies in character and slowly discovered what Owen was learning. They looked for scenes that were linked to specific emotions and watched Owen respond. Slowly, they entered Owen's world – and his mind. (Ron Suskind's moving 2016 documentary on this awakening is called *Life Animated.*)

After witnessing Owen's profound improvements, the Suskinds wanted to spread what they first termed "Disney Therapy." They later changed the name to "Affinity Therapy," discovering that other passions – Legos, train schedules, etc. are avenues into the lives of those on the spectrum. Affinities, Ron posits, are "pathways to both cognitive and emotional growth."

They are also important pathways for parents. Through these affinities, parents can express their love to their child and, in turn, receive it. I will be forever thankful for the divine timing of Ron and Cornelia Suskind in our life. Without their perseverance, we would never have deepened our understanding of Patrick.

Owen, a gifted artist, shared his drawing talent with Patrick, who, we found, also has a flair. They tapped into each other on many levels and, over the years, have formed a true and lasting friendship.

To this day, Owen often references Disney scenes and quotes characters' words – "You're not getting cold fins now, are you?" (Ariel from *The Little Mermaid.*) Or "You've got your own style, now let it shine through and remember no matter what, you've got to be you." (Sebastian from *The Little Mermaid.*) He is a master of everything Disney. Owen and Patrick found others at Riverview who also connect to these movies. Together, they formed "The Riverview Disney Club." Patrick's ability to play all the film's musical scores was a boon. When Riverview's musical director heard him play and sing, he all but said, "Thank you, God." And quickly handed Patrick the title of "Student Director."

Riverview's Disney Club met once a week and grew to over twenty-five people. Owen, the peer leader, would show a particular Disney movie and stop at selected scenes. He then opened a discussion about lessons embedded in each. "What can we learn from this?" he'd ask. Member's hands shot up. The excited chatter in the room was thrilling.

Disney movies are this group's field guide to life. It is their way to understand how to be in the world – how to engage with others and interpret emotions. If Disney made these movies to help people who do not have language or social skills, it would be called therapy.

And therapy it is! Being part of Disney Club discussions helps transform many quirks associated with people on the spectrum. Together with like-minded peers they break down barriers, which fosters connection. It expands communication and offers a road map to emotions. Disney movies model social behaviors and explain fundamental problems and resolutions. In them are lessons for life, even sage advice. And the surprise? Disney movies are not watched once and tucked away; they continue to instruct as the viewer matures. Peers help others come away feeling okay with the world.

At Riverview, Patrick reunited with Bobby, a friend dating back to preschool. They now vacation together with a special needs travel group. While they are close, they do not hold many conversations. But they do share Disney. When Bobby lost his mother, *The Lion King*'s overarching "Circle of Life" theme helped him process her untimely death. "I always know that my mom never leaves me," Bobby declared confidently. He and Patrick review that movie often, remembering other themes: the importance of friends and the wise "Rafikis" in our lives who help us through situations. Disney does in animation what we – parents, teachers, or therapists – could never do with words.

Disney Club was a huge part of Patrick's life. After Riverview ended, Patrick entered a nearby day program for others with autism. When the staff heard him reminisce about the Disney Club, they were fascinated and asked him to start one. A dream came true; Patrick wanted to establish a Disney Club everywhere.

He began another one at our local YMCA. In three years, it has grown to over twenty members and is facilitated by a co-teacher who is a school teacher by day.

Like many others on the spectrum, Patrick is involved in "Applied Behavior Analysis Therapy" (ABA). When staff in that group caught wind of Disney Club, they asked if he would run yet another one for them. There they spin the Disney lessons to cover even wider social and moral issues such as facing your fears, standing up for yourself, etc.

Patrick spends a lot of time preparing for these sessions, but his life does not center on Disney Club meetings. He is nearing the completion of his associate's degree in music from Quincy College. Six years ago, Patrick began chipping away at some of the more challenging classes. With support, he now manages two classes a semester. Several of those have ignited new interests. For example, history now fascinates him. And college Spanish courses have inspired him to learn other languages. (I find this a bit ironic since Patrick still can have challenges with English.) Math will be his most demanding course but getting the degree is the carrot!

It's not only Disney Club and college work that keeps Patrick busy. He composes music, writes songs, and plays "gigs." He is much more fluid writing songs than speaking.

Photograph, A Song by Patrick Birmingham

"Everywhere I go, every place I see
I always take my camera to places that matter to me.
In every single photograph, people say I've got a good eye,
but what I do is make the memories that I cherish every time."

Conveying what he wants to say and finding the right words in a conversation can be both tricky and time-consuming for him. As for his word choices, while appropriate, they are different. It can take a while for people to figure out what he is saying.

Patrick shares his passion for singing and playing music with his father. During the COVID-19 pandemic, the two played duets on our back porch to post on Facebook Live. (Yes, Patrick keeps up a Facebook page. It is packed with his top twenty Disney reviews, musical and Disney facts, and now, historical events of the day.) At one point in their duet, Patrick had to stop the music, and, in his calm loving way, correct Scott. Two adults! It was heartwarming to watch.

Patrick's musical skills may have sprung up from those early Bach, Beethoven, and Brahms days. We had that glimpse of something unique when he played Beethoven's Fifth at his keyboard. Others came in elementary school when teachers asked, "What *can't* he do?" A music instructor would play a series of notes and end with a random cord. Patrick could then spout the notes off effortlessly: "C, F, D sharp, A minor." Teachers might try to trick him again or shift the focus and ask him to play a song three scales below what they played. Most musicians would need time to reconfigure; Patrick could do it on the spot.

It was always his teachers who encouraged us to keep exploring his talents. Perfecting those of a performer has had its evolution. It started in third grade. Unbeknownst to me, Patrick's teacher put him in a talent show where he played "Tequila" to his first crowd of cheering fans. That led to enrolling him in music lessons. Those instructors and many at the South Shore Conservatory taught him finger skills and helped him incorporate more common techniques. During his middle and high school years, Patrick went to Derby Academy's Summer Arts Program. There he performed as a musician and improved as a vocalist. By summer's end, he was starring in bands and learning how to respond to standing ovations. Patrick had now gained a reputation and went on to participate in annual talent shows always receiving standing ovations.

Patrick is another "Wedding Singer," – able to play anything – and he is excellent party material. Recently, a neighbor asked him to play at her upcoming event. She had him learn fifteen new songs, many from the Frank Sinatra era. That night he soared; everyone was dancing. Guests began firing song titles at him and were astonished when Patrick performed them without hesitating. When they handed him a basket full of money at the end of the night, many shouted, "When can he play again?"

Yes, Patrick's days are full. He even makes time for daily exercise, meditation, and the ongoing 1000-piece puzzle in the living room. He has not stopped surprising me. A while back, I was told, "Wait 'til he is mid-twenties, there will be a big surge." It's true. All sorts of pieces are converging.

Looking at Patrick today, at age 27, people would have no idea how far he has come. A doctor once told me that Patrick might never talk, and early home videos reveal a vastly different person from who he is today. The changes are remarkable and thankfully point to a full life ahead. But this did not just happen. Every day of those twenty-seven years he has plugged away. Patrick earned where he is.

I plugged away as well and now see that there were sacrifices – our marriage of twenty-eight years for one. As a couple, we did not expect this, and we did not survive it.

Scott encouraged the strides Patrick made and the miracles that happened. But we differ and have grown apart. Scott would like to see Patrick squared away, living on his own and holding down a job. I, too, want Patrick to be independent, but I want to be realistic. Patrick is not ready. He still needs guidance, even prompts, to complete things. I worry, thinking of him navigating new situations. There are too many gaps in his overall comprehension of small and big things.

I often think every day is Groundhog Day in the life of someone with autism. I can say something to Patrick a thousand times only to find myself repeating it a day later. "Oh, I forgot," he says. For those reasons, Patrick will need support throughout his life. The pandemic has made me aware that I need to find the next living situation for him. God forbid I contract the virus, and Patrick is on his own. While he has matured and is much more aware of life's pitfalls, his safety and wellbeing in this troubled world are huge concerns.

Patrick's success comes from the thousands of things we tried and the endless "Rafikis" along the way. As the program director for The Arc of the South Shore's Autism Resource Center, I hear families say all the time, "I could never have done this without *them*." Raising a child on the spectrum does take a village!

I don't fully know how Patrick plots his course. I do not know what he expects from life, but I do know that the wish I had to connect with my son has been far more than a dream come true. Patrick talks of playing music and traveling the world. I see his passion and know he is eager to move in this direction, but he is also concerned about leaving me. I tell him I will be fine and that I support his dreams. What I do not tell him is that if he travels the world, "I'm coming!"

Betsy and Merriweather

Diagnosing a Girl with Autism

If girls are tricky to understand, girls with autism are real puzzles. Many are hiding in plain sight. They are better at masking the typical symptoms. Unlike boys, they do not fixate on odd things like train schedules. Instead, they are passionate about unicorns or horses, things not unexpected for girls.

Plenty of autistic stereotypes do not fit girls. They have better eye contact, they can share smiles, and they love to chum around. In fact, they *long* to fit in. Many are masters at mimicking other girls. They work hard at trying to imitate, but often they cannot pull it off. They do not understand the nuances. Innuendos go right over their head. The result? They become frustrated and disappointed. Eventually, they are rejected. Even sadder, many girls with autism remain undiagnosed – more often, misdiagnosed. Therein lies the tragedy. Without help, girls do not learn the strategies or coping skills they need. Such is the story of Merriweather.

Merri, my firstborn, came to me on angel's wings. She was super bright and curious, often awe-struck, and always delightfully happy. My husband, Jeremy, and I were thrilled. She met all her milestones on time and even talked early. At twelve weeks, Merri settled into daycare. Waddling around months later, she proved to be as huggable and sweet a child as could be. She would back up into me and plop into my lap – a virtual tap on the shoulder – "it's time to read a book." Merri loved jumping on her stuffed animals, biting their noses, and clawing at their eyes. She also loved her baths, her books, and her dad and mom. Of course, there were the usual childhood tantrums, but Merri was generally a very compliant child. She also had a definite personality. When her first brother, Wilton, came along, Merri declared, "Don lika de babe!" All was normal, or so we thought.

We did notice these odd little snippets – small nameless moments. But now, putting them all together, they paint a much clearer picture. Back then, I could always brush them off. Merri was afraid of loud noises, for example, but I figured most babies are. She also had a strong aversion to dogs. One appeared in our backyard one day, and I suggested we go say "Hi." But stepping outside, Merri's body stiffened, and a primal scream blared forth. *Dogs were not for everyone*, I thought. A third incident comes to mind. Before my second son, Oliver, was born, we visited Jeremy's aunt, who had a friend visiting from England. Ray was a rather large, heavy man with a long thick beard. Merri, visibly anxious, couldn't be around him. We chalked it up to his size, his accent, and the beard. In all these situations, we comforted her; we never made them into big deals. Yet, now, seventeen years later, I wonder, *should I have spent more time analyzing them?*

Her early school years presented other harbingers of things to come. In preschool, I had to peel Merri off me at the classroom door. Is this the anxiety that weighs her down today? Back then, I shook it off, comforted seeing other children entering the classroom in tears.

All these were juxtaposed to Merri's more precious moments. Chatting away in her car seat once, she stopped for a minute, then blurted out, "That's raponious." She was mimicking my well-worn-out phrase, "That's ridiculous." Another time, when Merri had a cold, she stopped me while reading her a story and reported,

"Mommy, there's no wind from my nose!" A more exemplary picture of my Merri was painted when I took her to meet her preschool teacher. Mrs. Sanders bent down and asked, "How would you like me to introduce you to the class? Should we call you Merri or Merriweather?" Without a moment's hesitation, Merri declared, "You can call me Mrs. Bat Mermaid."

Here was my spirited, sensitive little girl. She had a sparkling imagination and lived in an animated, often ethereal reality. Nothing about her hinted of trouble, far from it. If anything, Jeremy and I were sure her bright light would burn even brighter when nourished by teachers and friends.

Our hopes were to shatter. Halfway through kindergarten, the teacher asked the class to write their name. With a moniker like Merriweather Eschelbacher, Merri looked up and said, "No." Her "No" meant "I don't know *how*." I get that now. I didn't then. What I did get was an email from her teacher. Her answer to Merri's "No?" Put her in a corner, away from classmates, hand her a pencil and a piece of paper, and plunk down a timer. Merri returned home frazzled.

This was to be the start of hundreds of emails throughout Merri's school years. In first grade, Mrs. Murray asked Jeremy and me to come in. She wanted to illustrate one of Merri's problems. She told us of a drawing assignment the class was given and then presented Merri's picture. While the picture was not on topic, it was also not psychopathic. The two of us were awed by it, remarking, "Man, does she have a beautiful mind." Mrs. Murray continued to address her concerns, ones we already heard in kindergarten. "Merri has poor handwriting, she doesn't complete her work, she's easily distracted, and she talks a lot." "Okay, "we thought, "she's six, for goodness sake." Nonetheless, we asked Mrs. Murray what the next steps should be. Merri needed more help, she thought, but not an all-out Individual Education Plan (IEP).

Jeremy and I put our heads together. If we were to find help for Merri with those early academic concepts, she will whiz through her worksheets. We sent her to the Kumon Center for Reading and Math a few towns over. Immediately, our lives were hell. Even though they taught using simple steps, Merri did not do the work. The work? One page with six questions. Six! There was plenty of teeth-gnashing for the next several months. Finally, we realized that we were killing ourselves; Kumon was not going to help, and I couldn't keep up the good fight. I was now on bed rest expecting our newest surprise, Eliot.

In second grade, the school encouraged us to fill out the Connors form. (A Connors Parent Rating Scale (CPRS) is one of three forms used to assess Attention Deficit Hyperactivity Disability, better known as ADHD.) I learned of Dr. Slater, a psychiatrist who worked with children. I asked her what tests I should request for Merri. The school administered the usual battery of psych-ed tests along with the BASC 2 (Behavior Assessment System for Children). The results confirmed our pediatrician's diagnosis of ADHD. Dr. Slater then explained ADHD to us, ticking off the various traits. As she went on, I thought, *Wait a minute. This is ME*! I later had that diagnosis confirmed. Like mother like daughter.

"Okay, because of her ADHD," said the school, "we will start her on a 504 Plan." "Great," we sighed in relief, "a 504 – some support is coming!" But nothing changed. Instead, teachers barraged us with complaints about Merri's other shortcomings. "She is not completing her work." "She does this when she needs to be doing that." Always followed by, "She's not living up to her potential!" And every year, they would add, "Her handwriting is terrible." We never questioned if these problems stemmed from ADHD. Her doctor stated that there was a high correlation between poor penmanship and ADHD. Why would we look any further?

Jeremy stepped up. As a high school physics teacher, he was

home at 3:00 and could help Merri before leaving for his second job. We were happy to walk this path with Merri, for a bit. But the goal of the 504 plan, we assumed, was to equip her with skills and then help her apply them. Soon she would lift off from us and manage on her own. As for Merri's inattentiveness? The school's answer was medication. I was terribly conflicted, but we tried it. Then, we took her off, put her back on, and finally stopped it for all sorts of reasons: not sleeping for one. She was not a distraction or a "problem child" in the classroom. She was off somewhere in that creative mind of hers, perhaps reviewing thoughts of her "yesternights." I reckoned they needed her to conform in the classroom so the teacher could get *her* work done. My plea was always, "Work with her. She is a square peg trying to fit into *your* round hole."

There were classroom issues and homework concerns, but we had more significant problems in our sights. Merri was continuously frustrated with classmates, teachers, and friends. Making a friend had always been challenging. She couldn't navigate relationships. She would arrive home in tears, saying "I don't understand why they said they wanted to sit with me at lunch and then didn't." Or she'd whimper, "I asked this person if they wanted to play at recess. Then when recess came, they went and played with someone else and didn't invite me." My nature is to dole out solutions, but now I realize Merri was confused and probably just wanted to talk about it.

I tried to help her fit in, dressing her in the cutest outfits I could find. We did the sleepovers and birthday parties, but *we* were the ones doing the inviting. Our phone was not ringing off the hook for her. When each new school year began, play dates came in, but they soon fizzled out. We did not put it together back then; we had no time. Jeremy was working two jobs; I was also working full time and had two other babies. We could only plug the dikes.

I was aware of a core group of girls in Merri's class. She talked nonstop about them. Merri joined them. Soon she became peripheral and then overlooked. We still invited them to her birthday party every March. A telling incident happened at one. Merri, surrounded by a chatty group, interrupted, and asked an out-of-the-blue question, "What is your favorite color?" They shook their heads, rolled their eyes, and moved away. I knew that sometimes her mind could be quirky that way, so can mine.

Friends might have come and gone. And they always did. But we found comfort remembering she had brothers. Merri knew that she was their great poohbah. "I want to play dress up and paint your nails," she would announce. I'd hear them shout, "ME TOO!" Her brother, Will, often found his hair coiffed and ladened with barrettes. Anything she wanted to do, they did. If there were a cardboard box, a rock, and a crown, she would put it together and entertain them for hours. I thought Merri was like me. I, too, leaned toward hanging around with the boys.

Throughout their childhoods, I was always on the lookout for new activities. I wanted them to meet different people and take on new challenges. After second grade, Merri participated in Old Sturbridge Village's summer camp. She dressed in the colonial period, played 3-legged sack races, and milked cows. She loved everything about it and even made a friend.

Other summers, my in-laws took the children for a week and sent them to camp in Marblehead. Merri enjoyed all the typical outdoor activities. Once, she signed up for "Drama," which meant participating in an end-of-the-week production. When we arrived for the performance, we heard, "Merri quit." The buildup during the week was too much. She could not do it. I sensed others were judging her; they did not understand that her anxiety was real. I was on high alert for anyone humiliating Merri; she had enough of that at school. While we saw that she was willing to try new things, we also saw the ensuing anxiety. I did shame repair for years.

Merri might have had some quirky behaviors and a few school issues, but we found she also had genuine fears. She're-fused to play the game *Operation* because the body parts disturbed her. Merri even hated Halloween. Once, in late October, she went to a birthday party at a boy's house. I had to go back and pick her up. She was in tears; they had a skeleton. Since she was in first grade, I thought she would outgrow it.

However, we could never have scary decorations; we always had to have a smiling skeleton or a happy witch. One house in our neighborhood went insane with decorations every Halloween. We called it "The Creepy House." It was top-notch scary. We knew Merri would not go near it. One night, talking about it at dinner, she piped up, "Oh yeah, I just move to the other side of the bus, so I don't have to look." I was impressed with her strategy. But I was concerned that Merri was avoiding and making her world smaller.

While the family saw that Merri's fears were real, we also saw the drama that swirled around her. It seemed to follow her. Merri would perseverate on an event or a person, stirring up such anxiety until it spilled into a river of tears. I did not understand why these incidents rocked her off her foundation. Try as I did, I didn't know how else to frame things. So, I taught her the Serenity prayer thinking it would help slow her down long enough to discern what to do.

The dramas mounted. The crescendo was about to erupt. As a family, when Merri was nine or ten, we read the Harry Potter series. She started rereading them on her own. But, one day, in the middle of one, she decided to pick up a completely different book, *The Lightning Thief.* In seconds, she plunked it down, announcing, "I can't read that. I would make Harry Potter upset." I stood stock-still. This was not one of those small nameless moments; this was sobering. She was for real. Something new was happening. We needed help.

We were referred to another therapist who put Merri's escalating anxiety in focus for us. Over countless Saturday mornings, she taught Merri coping skills. We soon saw they were working. One night, for example, there was a loud noise in her room, and she talked herself off that ledge. The therapist also gave us assignments to help desensitize Merri's fears. "First, go to Target and stand in the Halloween aisle." Next, go often and stand across the street from "The Creepy House." Somehow it worked. Merri *trick-or-treated* that year as a scary character. She also braved "The Creepy House," which was even more revved up. Dracula was out front in a hearse, and worse, a dummy in a chair vomited into a trash can when you passed. Merri walked right by! The perk? They gave out huge boxes of candy.

Merri had overcome her Halloween fears, we thought, but not her relentless histrionics. One was in plain sight the night of the big fourth-grade concert. Since Merri had to be there early, I dropped her off along with her trombone. When I returned with the family, a swarm of girls stood around her. It reeked of "Poor Merri – the victim." In near hysteria, she told me she had forgotten her music. The scene repelled me, but since it was already in full swing, I rolled my eyes and let it unfold. Episodes like this were now multiplying. This was one more for her therapist.

The high drama and troubling school issues became very clear. So did our inability to manage her. Jeremy and I spent a lot of time talking about Merri, trying to figure her out. We encouraged riding lessons and soccer, but after a short time, we would hear, "Nah, I don't want to do that." We suggested basketball. She seemed excited. But we saw that she is not terribly coordinated, and between everyone screaming and the music blaring, she couldn't take it. Nothing ever fit for her. I bought her knitting needles once – that lasted a minute. She tried afterschool activities, Newspaper Club for one. That ended in disaster as well. She told us that she was not interested in it, but today I know it was self-protection. She did not have the skills. She had to quit.

Fifth grade, marking the end of elementary school, is a big deal. It wrapped up with two events. The first was a field trip to Boston's George's Island – straight-up anxiety for me. I was hoping she would have fun and worried she would not. One of the class mothers on the trip kept an eye out for me. Merri just wanted to be included, so before the trip, I got her an iPad to be on Instagram like everyone else. That was a mistake. If Merri did not understand how life as a pre-teen works, it was torturous for her to watch it on a screen. Keep in mind that parents post pictures of their children. I'd see them. *I talked to that mom the other day*; I would think. *She never mentioned this,* or *Why wasn't Merri invited to that?*

The concluding event for fifth grade is "Recognition Night." Jeremy and I prepared and thought we knew how it was going to go down. We tried our best to help Merri sort out her expectations for the big night. There would be awards: "Best Reader," "Best Artist," "Best Mathematician," etc. Those, we knew, were not going to go to her. But students, we later learned, could nominate themselves for an award *they* thought they deserved. Without a word to anyone, Merri went ahead and wrote a description of what hers should be. That night my in-laws came as did her brothers, who were all gussied up. I, of course, was a wreck! The curtain opened, and there was Merri placed smack dab in the center of the front row. There she sat. For the whole forty-five minutes, Merri sat. She never *had* to get up; she received no award, no recognition, no mention. *Nothing.*

A few mothers came up to us afterward. They remarked on how composed Merri was despite looking like she was on the verge. Jeremy and I had to muddle through for her, so we went to the after-party, where it went from bad to worse. In front of us, the core group of girls gathered arm in arm to have their pictures taken. Nobody asked Merri to join them. We quickly said our goodbyes politely and found the door. Arriving home, Merri let it all out, "I wanted one thing, ONE thing, I wanted to be recognized for one thing!" She was about to combust. I could only emphasize how loving and kind she always is and how these awards are not what makes life meaningful. She couldn't hear it. I had to walk away; Jeremy stayed.

The next day, hysterically crying, I laid into the principal. "Do you know where Merri and I are every Saturday? We are in therapy, not out playing soccer or basketball like everyone else. We are in therapy. And you put her in the front row knowing she is not going to get a damn thing? Are you kidding me? Can anyone stand here and tell me where we are racing to? Where is my child in this race? Nowhere. She is smart, she gets good grades, but she has no friends. She doesn't understand why nobody likes her or why they don't want to be with her. And this race? None of it matters if my child is shattered." "You're right! We can do better," he responded. I turned around and closed the door. Elementary school had ended.

Sometime that summer, our family sat around the firepit with close friends, and another incident revealed why Merri gets snubbed. All of a sudden, our friend's son hollered in frustration, "Merri, you already said that!" Three times she had repeated, "I like Marshmallows." I looked at Jeremy, started laughing, and answered, "Yeah, she does that!" I could relate; I am not a great conversationalist. It was easy to chalk that one up to youth. She was also only eleven, after all.

Before Merri went into any new grade, Jeremy and I made a point to meet with her teachers. Going into sixth grade, we learned Merri would have to move between classes. I thought this will be a fabulous way for her to get her wiggles out. A bigger school also meant more activities. And, with ninety to a hundred classmates, there would be more friends. We were hopeful; she was excited.

Academically Merri did fine. She made the honor roll every year. While that was wonderful, it also felt misleading. Her success was a direct result of our intervention. We hired a tutor at school to help her get work done. Jeremy was her scaffolding at home, breaking each project down. I was her cheerleader and the pillar she could lean on. Merri could do the academic part well enough but not the planning. Again, we wondered, *Where are these strategies she is supposed to be learning? And when are her teachers going to start integrating them?*

This school was big on sports, and there were a lot of good athletes. Merri was not one of them. But gym class introduced her to hiking. It became her passion. "Let's go!" she said eagerly one fall day. "I want to take you on this hike." Off we went to Wachusett Reservoir. All we heard the whole way around was, "Look at this! Look over there, look at that!" Her exhilaration was infectious. Jeremy and I were thrilled. Then a few weeks later, she declared, "I hate hiking!" Why was it that everything starts with a burst of "Merri enthusiasm?" Then, the bottom drops out, and the excitement is over.

At the start of each school year, she was usually invited to a lot of things. So, I watched and waited. For the initial six weeks, Merri put all her effort into getting to know people. She seemed to do well. But soon, everything became too taxing. School, the classes, the people – it was not fun anymore; it was not new. What's more, her classmates began slogging away, getting the work done. Merri could not push through it. She didn't know how. We did not know that she was lost, and frankly, neither did she.

One of the early invitations came for a birthday party. It was in late October and warm enough to be outside. I drove her there and scanned the place, of course, looking for possible (Halloween) triggers. I noticed a wooden playhouse turned into a pirate ship. It had the skull and crossbones but nothing scary. I left only to get the call, "Everything is okay, but Merri doesn't want to go outside." My heart broke. Like "The Creepy House," Merri developed a way to avoid it. She hung inside, befriended the dog, played pool with his sister but did not join the party. It could have been a case of overwhelming social anxiety or a mix of too many children. But her Halloween fears came back. Sadly, she did not reach for the coping skills I thought were in place.

We moved on; we had to. Next, we learned that Merri had developed a crush on a boy. She announced that she wanted to go to the sixth-grade dance. While unexpected, it was an exciting step. It seemed she had a good time, but Merri was never one to rush home gushing. Instead, I got a call the next day from a friend. "I want to let you know there was some theatrics at the dance." "Oh no, what?" I asked. "Merri told everyone that she was bisexual. Then she asked a girl to dance, and drama ensued." I am not one to respond to things lightly, so when Jeremy came home, I spewed this mess all over him until he said, "Who cares?" I stopped, thought for a second, and said, "You are right. It doesn't matter." We left it alone. Maybe I shouldn't have.

That was the year she got her hair cut. She pranced into the house practically bald. "Cute," I said and meant it. "But now we need earrings." "Why?" asked Merri. "Because you look like a boy." So, she got her ears pierced and came home, keen to call all sorts of people, people who were barely her friends. But before the year was over, she let the piercings close. I wondered why until I thought that *I*, too, am all about "No Maintenance." But this time, she was not taking after me. I realize today that changing earring all the time is exhausting when you are working so hard just to keep pace.

That June, we sent the three oldest away to camp. Merri had a great time and made friends. She would; it was only two weeks. Her counselor took me aside when we picked them up and said, "She's so lovely; it was great she was here." Peers cause Merri problems, not adults. Adults warm to her. She is articulate and brilliantly creative. She is also well-read, polite, and funny.

She has always been funny. Back in second-grade phonics class, the teacher talked about "the wedding" of the letters Q and

U. Merri, arriving home ecstatic, said she wanted to wear her pink dress the next day to the wedding. Another time, before dinner, I said, "Let's say our prayer." Merri sprung up, "I'll say the prayer!" She put her hand over her heart and recited *The Pledge of Allegiance,* which she had just learned. Everyone in my family knew she was funny, but I don't think peers hung around long enough to experience it.

Summer was coming to an end. A family camping trip to Maine was on the calendar. Perfect time to get away and get ready for school. Seventh grade for Merri was two weeks away. We pulled into our site and set up camp. The first morning, I woke to Jeremy's moaning. I nudged him once. Then again. The moaning stopped. Jeremy had died.

My husband was in great shape; everyone knew that. After all, he was a vegetarian and a marathon runner. His primary doctor even said to him at his last appointment, "If I had more patients like you, I would be out of business." But Jeremy had a widow's maker heart.

I was devastated. We were all in shambles. People were kind and took care of us. Many brought food and friends took all four children school shopping. The boys, still in elementary school, had teachers who enveloped them. Merri was in a different school. She was steady enough to go to classes and even held up hearing a comment from a boy who sat down next to her. "You're one parent away from being Batman." I later learned that Batman was an orphan.

That year, academics for Merri started out fine, but again her grades plunged. At home, things were a little chaotic. Before our camping trip, Jeremy was in the middle of a massive renovation project. Our house was cut in two, leaving an enormous hole in the ground between the structures – a footprint for a large deck. Inside was nearly uninhabitable, with wires and plastic sheeting hanging everywhere.

While I supposedly got up each morning, I had no idea what I was doing. I did hear Merri! She came home so angry, so often. She was hyper-reactive to classmates complaining about their dads. In the same breath, she uttered, "I miss my dad." I tried many times to work it through with her but finally said emphatically, "I get it! I do! But it is not ever going to be. You are always going to have a dead father now. I cannot change that. Even if he were alive, you wouldn't always like him. You'd be complaining too." But Merri's fury only grew, pushing me and others further away.

In October, we joined a bereavement group. Merri met peers who also experienced the death of a parent. We went twice a month for three years. Often Merri did not want to go. It was rough going. She soon became combative.

One of the women in our group mentioned that her father died when she was twelve. "Our family fell apart," she told us. Determined that would not happen to us, I announced at dinner one night, "We are not going to fall apart!" Merri pushed the chair out from under her, stood up, and began yelling, "How dare you say that?" She shouted about how horrible a mother I am and then raged about how awful I treat her. It was nonstop until she stormed off, leaving all three boys crying hysterically. Life was to go downhill from there.

I was in constant contact with her guidance counselor. But the dial did not move for Merri. Jeremy and I knew that each of our children would have different intellectual needs. We were adamant that we would do whatever it took to meet them. I was taking a page from that playbook when I investigated "School Choice" – a *fresh start*, I thought. *A bigger school, more kids to choose from, more clubs, and great afterschool activities.* I was sure this was the answer.

Off Merri went to Hudson High School for eighth grade. Again, we enjoyed the six to eight-week honeymoon period. She made friends – well, questionable friends. Things she told me about them made the hair on the back of my neck stand up. But, by now, I knew the pattern anyhow. Those friends would disappear. Then her complaints would start about the bus driver, teachers, classmates. Everything was always everyone else's fault.

Her frustration intensified and began cascading into other areas. Samantha, the director of our bereavement center, called. "Merri needs far more than our group. She is disruptive and antagonistic. She is not working well with others." Samantha ended by recommending a therapist. We sought her out immediately.

Along with Merri grousing about people and things, she also talked a lot about gender that year. She is trans, she told me. I have to say I was not kind, "What do you mean you're trans? I am dealing with all this, and now you tell me you think you're trans?" I did not think it was real but called a friend whose daughter is now a son. I made tracks with Merri out to Worcester to see his gender therapist. Then we drove to Marlboro for her regular counseling. Add in the bereavement group. After a while, I find that I am spending all my time at appointments but seeing no improvement. One grey area did eventually settle. Merri, and her gender counselor, concluded that she is not trans.

Clearing up the gender issue gave us a breather. It was short-lived. Merri's grades were plummeting. I called an "educational coach," a private tutor, and divulged the problems we were having. He said he could help. He worked with her for a very pricey six months only to come back to me saying, "It's not working. She is not changing, and she is verbally aggressive."

Merri has become a frequent flier at the school's guidance office, seeing a young intern who, I learned, was gay. It was this intern who had been handing Merri the pamphlets on being trans. I called a meeting. I not only wanted the brochures to stop, but I also wanted them to get into high gear with academic support.

While that was supposedly underway, another call came from the school. This time it was not about Merri's work or class behavior.

They explained, "We have Merri with us. You need to bring her to the ER for an evaluation. She has a plan to commit suicide." When questioned in the car, Merri answered, "I could never do that to you, Mom. You lost Dad!" After six hours, the doctors deemed her all right, but it left me to watch her.

I looked around. I saw all my boys walking on eggshells, wondering what Merri would do next. And there was always a "next." Soon enough, she strolled in and revealed an illegal tattoo. I was so furious that I took her down to the police station, hoping they would read her the riot act. That didn't faze her at all. *"What was it going to take,"* I wondered?

Angry? Yes. But nothing compared to learning that Merri failed eighth grade. I watched her bottom out the first term and requested that her 3-year evaluation be moved up to February. It was May when the evaluation was completed, and those disparate scores determined that she now qualified for an IEP. *Duh*, I thought. *A little too late!* I was provided with the option of "socially promoting" her. I took it because an IEP meant "therapeutic, academic support services." (TASS)

She soon became a TASS Office frequent flier. Merri would come home complaining that all they did for her was encourage her to get her back to the classroom. While confused at first, I finally understood. They are there to get the students educated, not to get them whole. They did, however, make a plan. Merri would stay after school to complete work with her different teachers. But soon, Merri started blowing that off. I was losing hope.

November of that year, I asked for a meeting. They scheduled it for January. Merri failed her first semester and was on her way to failing her second. When I asked the group, "What are *we* doing to help her?" the same old replies came. I left the meeting and called an educational advocate.

Home, meanwhile, was becoming less and less of a happy place. There was mounting stress and constant fighting. Merri then began to refuse to go to school. Administrators suggested they talk to her first thing in the morning. We did this for a week. Then I realized my other three are going to start trying to get away with it too. I could not let that happen. It didn't matter. Merri stopped going to school anyway.

I asked for another meeting, and my advocate took charge. She marched in and declared, "You are not meeting Merri's needs." Their answer? "We will put her in a lower level." *Drop her again?* I thought. *More shame? I remembered the carrel they put around her desk and the string they used around her ankles to keep her from fidgeting. She is near the end, and she is failing. They want to push her through.* That meeting produced nothing but more worry. Then came another blow. Merri failed ninth grade.

My advocate suggested I pursue a private neuro-psych test for Merri. It verified ADHD. Her scores, showing even further disparity, secured an out-of-district school placement for her. Hopeful, we chose Orchard Street Academy in Marlboro for her second tour of ninth grade. We liked both the principal and the fact that Merri would be assigned a clinician. I had no expectations. By now, I knew there was no panacea.

Merri made some friends, but six weeks in – the same old story – the invitations stopped. I expected that. I did not expect the same old complaints. When they began, and everything was someone else's fault, I thought, *I cannot do this! No one in my house has smiled for years, and Merri is not getting what she needs!*

Emails from teachers began again, too. "Can you work with Merri to get her classwork done? She's having trouble focusing." I had to ask myself, *why are we at a different school getting the same answers? You said you could manage this!* I also got calls from the school saying, "I don't think it's real, but I thought you should know Merri is talking about taking a bottle of pills." High alert, again.

In early December, we headed to Maine to spend the Hanukkah weekend with family. None of the cousins have electronics. I knew I had to plant the seed for this, so I greeted my children morning, noon, and night. "Don't forget we are going to Auntie's on Saturday…. no phones! I love you." Saturday came. The boys piled in the car with books, pillows, Mad Libs, and decks of cards. Merri came out with a backpack filled with electronics.

It was tempting to leave a fifteen-year-old home. Instead, I made Merri sit in the way back, so I didn't have to interact with her. I spent the two-hour drive thinking. *I am the same mother to these four children. Three out of the four have no problems. What is going on here? What am I not seeing? What is it that Merri does not understand? And why doesn't she understand?* There is something more here. This is now bigger than me and much bigger than her. I did everything, but now my toolbox is empty.

The following week we had a med check with Merri's psychiatrist, and I shared these new reflections. The doctor agreed, saying, "I am thinking partial hospitalization." "I am not thinking partial anything," I blurted out. "I am thinking therapeutic boarding school. She has become defiant and angry, and nobody can fix this."

Through an acquaintance and a series of phone calls, I found Wilderness Therapy in Utah. I phoned and gave the Wilderness director a bird's eye view of Merri. "I can help your daughter," she said. "Really," I replied, a bit snarky. "Because I can't even tell you how many people have said they can help my daughter. And they haven't, so to say I am a little skeptical is an understatement." "No, I *can* help your daughter." "Really?" I asked more humbly. "Yes," she repeated, "I can."

The calendar still read December. Can I make this happen? And soon? The program was pricier than any prestigious New England prep school. I was not back to work yet and am using Jeremy's life insurance to raise my family. There was no other choice. Stabilizing Merri's mental health was paramount.

I enrolled her on December 21st, having now accepted that Merriweather's academic career was not going to look like anyone else's. I faked my way through Christmas, and on December 27th, not even three weeks after our trip to Maine, I told Merri we were going off for a "grand adventure in Utah."

She had no idea what was coming. Merri had her head buried in her phone. She did ask a couple of questions on the plane, but the little I said led to visions of a ski trip. We arrived at the hotel where the transport team met us in the morning. It all happened fast. The driver took Merri's meds from me. I reached to hug her and then watched as the van pulled away. Merri was now on the ride to save her life.

I went back to our room, screamed, cried, and swore at my husband, "I can't believe I have to do this by myself. I can't believe this is my life!" I spent the rest of the day back and forth with Leigh, a seasoned, twenty-year clinician at Wilderness.

After the initial intake, Merri was outfitted with all the gear she would need. Everything from a camp stove and plates to clothes and a backpack. Despite the plunging December temperatures, she was to live outdoors until April. She and ten girls set out, accompanied by field guides. They were each responsible for rationing their food and cooking their separate meals. Each night the group bedded down somewhere new. The field guides, with eyes wide open, reported daily to individual clinicians. They, in turn, might suggest new strategies. Once a week, the group would come in from the field to take a five-minute cold shower and restock.

Group therapy, based on the 360-degree model, also took place at that time. The field guides talked openly about each girl. The individual then commented, and the clinician ended by summarizing what she heard. The girls received support to manage the challenges, never were they shamed. Merri's first test, repacking her backpack, came early the very first day. Each item had to be folded and packed in a particular order, or the bag would not close. No surprise that she screamed in frustration. The surprise was that she loved it.

Within a matter of weeks, Leigh called me. "Have you ever had her tested for autism? She hasn't connected with anyone all this time." "Nope," I replied. "Girls," she went on, "present differently than boys. They also get misdiagnosed with depression, anxiety, and ADHD. We need to have her tested." She ended by saying, "I have been doing this for a long time, and I am *never* wrong. I guarantee you she has autism."

Merri's test happened in the field. Sure enough, results placed her *on the spectrum.* Merri did not want this label mentioned to anyone. The diagnosis sent waves of relief over me as well as deep sadness. How could so many people – educators, therapists, doctors, tutors – have missed this? *No wonder she was lonely. No wonder she never connected with peers,* I thought. *No wonder, no wonder, no wonder – schoolwork, social cues, the drama! It all fits now.* I looked back. We had spoken with everyone and done everything we could. But it was right in front of us the whole time, camouflaged by the wrong diagnosis.

With this new label, Leigh said she needed to figure out what should be next for Merri. I did not know there was to be a "next." I assumed Wilderness would fix her, Merri would return home, and we would live happily ever after. That was not to be.

It was recommended that I hire an educational consultant to identify the best placement for Merri. In collaboration with Leigh, they identified three therapeutic schools. The first – a co-ed school – was eliminated immediately. The second one was too. It was industrial looking on the outside and had frightening behaviors inside. Kolob Canyon Residential Treatment Center was small, intimate, and homey. It also offered a wide range of therapeutic activities.

There were now four weeks between finishing Wilderness and starting at Kolob. One of the things I learned through working with Leigh was that Merri, like most individuals on the spectrum, needs time to process things. A move like this was a big deal, and Wilderness got it right. Leigh placed her in a position of leadership. Knowing she thrives in the role of "Been there, done that; I can help you," I watched as Merri came into her own.

Before Merri left home, everything was *my* fault. And while Merri had softened some over the past five months, things still felt strained despite having done some rigorous exercises. One included writing letters to each other that were filtered by her clinician. Leigh coached me not to engage in any of the blame that came up. Merri continued in her group while I discussed her progress with her clinician. I learned that Merri still needs help, especially when it comes to relationships. Ours is still unfolding.

Enduring the outdoors and learning responsibility did not break her. It stabilized her. She needed that time to decompress, to shake it all out, and calm raw nerves. New skills gave her emotional fortitude and restored her confidence. She even worked through a stormy relationship with a peer, Maize, to form a true friendship. Maize sent her a birthday card after leaving the program. Nobody has ever sent Merri a birthday card.

After her graduation on April 9th, Merri was dropped off at that same hotel and into my hands. She immediately luxuriated in both a hot shower and a soothing bath. Friends and relatives weighed in, saying, "Oh great, she's finished. You can go shopping and get your nails done." But after being in the backwoods for so long, there were many sensitivities. Artificial light made her squint, for example. Her food intake was different; she could not run out and eat a cheeseburger and fries. We had to take things slowly.

Before graduation, they warned me to prepare for any possible scenario. Merri was not someone I worried about running on me, but I wondered how she would be without her beloved iPhone. Thankfully, we made it through. Merri slept in a real bed, and we woke early to drive the four hours to Kolob.

The school had sent me a list of "preferred clothing," nothing with ties or strings. Kolob also wanted these girls dressed modestly and without makeup. Merri's things were inventoried and put away. We made her bed, fluffed up her pillows, and topped it off with her "Lamby." It was time for me to leave; Merri was embarking on her next journey.

Kolob life is a combination of school and therapy. There are activities such as horseback riding, yoga, and journaling on top of a full academic course load. There is also personal time and morning and evening chores. Duties assigned in the stable with a dozen horses and several foals were Merri's favorite. The long, pro-grammed days eased up on Wednesdays for so-called "Adventure Days." From 8:30 to 5, depending on the weather, they hiked or volunteered at either an animal shelter or a food pantry. Once a month, they left on a Tuesday and returned Thursday for a loaded, three-day, sleepaway adventure.

Kolob's enrollment is small; twelve girls in three bedrooms. They get moved around often depending on the "level" one is on. Different levels have different privileges. You would think Merri would look for those "bennies." But in typical adolescent fashion, Merri tested the limits early on by not doing her homework. She was used to punishment, but nobody at Kolob had to use it. Con-sequences there are clear. Nothing is negotiable. That fifteen minutes of personal time? No homework? The answer was simple, "Sorry, you lost that privilege." Part of their treatment is to help the girls realize that life is not a fight. You do not argue about what you have to do, what time things are, or what is for dinner.

Class size is small, and all are on different grade levels. Merri might be doing tenth-grade work in history and ninth-grade work in math. This fits her. So does Kolob's therapeutic approach, known as DBT (Dialectical Behavior Therapy). Merri soon expe-rienced those aha moments, "Oh, this is why I did that." And with insight came acceptance. She is okay with her diagnosis now and is willing to learn coping skills. Key has been learning to pause, then identify what is going on. She is also better able to manage the sudden surges of emotions that used to provoke her to jump from one crisis to another. Now she focuses on "staying in her own lane" and controlling what she can. Merri's anxiety can flare being with others who know more than she does. She is now able to accept that some things come easy, others do not. She understands that there will always be people ahead and behind her. Using DBT's mindfulness training, Merri is learning to sit in the discomfort.

The concept of "staying in her own lane" also applies to the area that troubles her most – connecting with others. She has learned that it does not matter what Susie Q is doing. It does not matter if Susie Q is spiteful or if her friend is yours. Merri has moved mountains pushing through this work. Connections with others, she now knows, may or may not happen. They might even be iffy. She manages that discomfort by staying in the moment, focusing on what is in her control and what is not. It's a practice. Merri is not perfect, and staff knows that. But they check in and strategize with her. They are kind but can also be straightforward, "Merri, cut the bull and get your act together!"

Merri started with C's her first semester. Kolob's education director pushed her, saying, "You can do better." Usually, if told to do something, Merri will shut down. This time, she called me. I had one answer. "The goal is to grow a whole human being, Merri. I am not looking for A's or even B's. If your grades are C's, that's fine. Just do your best." The second semester, and every semester since then, Merri has gotten straight A's. She is still not going to Harvard, but the changes are encouraging. She reads for pleasure now, and not long ago, she announced that she wanted to audit a history class. That's different!

Kolob's education is all I could have hoped for her. Last October was their parent-teacher conference. I held back tears as I stood to say, "Merri has had nothing but a school history of one trauma after another. She was never good enough, 'You never finish your work, you never do this, never do that, never, never, never. You're terrible, terrible, terrible all the way through.' You have all worked to develop true relationships with her. That's the reason she can be successful."

Merri graduated in November 2020 and is now in a "step down" program. Life with training wheels. I have gone to see her alone a couple of times, and once, I took the boys. She began coming home monthly for a few days last fall. Then COVID-19 hit. After six months of quarantining, Merri will now come for longer stretches. I have to say that these visits are never relaxing; there is a bit of PTSD involved, and I become hypervigilant. She continues to have trouble being parented. And trust between us is still being repaired. Not long ago, she went for a bike ride. Later she shared that when she got around the corner, the thought flashed; *I am gonna take off my helmet.* But she stopped herself and said, *"No, I am not going to do that because my word is important, and I said I would wear my helmet."*

Putting someone back together again is much more complicated than keeping them whole in the first place. Having gained a deeper understanding of herself, Merri has found peace. She is becoming that whole human. And while she still challenges me, I, too, have learned to stop, think, and try different approaches. Our family is a unit once again.

I had one local school meeting while Merri was in Utah. They contend that she does not need residential and insist they can help her. I disagree. She has come too far to be flung back into a pressure cooker high school for the year and a half she has left. It is going to be an uphill battle. I have made peace with the fact that I may never get that money back. I had to save her life.

We will have another mountain to climb when she comes home. And more work to do. There is always room to grow. I did not know what I was doing before. I know Merri now. A good friend visited when she was home and remarked, "She's back.

She's changed, but she's still Merri." It's true. I see her creativity; I hear her humor, and I know her caring. Merri's light shines brightly again. She is empowered.

Postscript: Merri's story did not begin with the right diagnosis; it ended with it. That may be familiar to the many young girls who have been misdiagnosed or left undiagnosed. But Merri's journey is her own. It is unique and not a prescription for an Outward-Bound type of experience. Fortunately, today – ten to twelve years after Merri's challenges in public schools – teachers, doctors, and therapists are more informed about how autism presents in girls and can provide more local support. Parents with children on the spectrum can also access ABA therapy which individualizes treatment to specific needs. (As of August 2019, all 50 states and Washington, D.C. have mandates that require some level of insurance coverage for the treatment of autism.)

Danielle and Johnny & Bella

Siblings on the Spectrum: Level One Autism & Non-verbal Autism with Global Cognitive Delay

You would think that my vocation and years of training in "emergency preparedness" would have equipped me for challenges in my own life. But having children two years apart brought new meaning to the word, "prepared." Add autism to the mix, and one's life can flip upside down. That is what happened to my husband Paul and me.

For years, I was the security manager for a large hospital and oversaw all safety personnel. I was also responsible for emergency management, including disaster planning. I hoped this would lead to a career as a police officer, but I let go of that dream when I learned I was pregnant. I knew my life was going to change – it was no longer all about me.

My firstborn, Johnny, arrived in October 2009. All seemed normal even though he walked a little later than most. But at two, he was only using a few words. So, we decided to see what the Autism Resource Center at the Arc of the South Shore had to say about that. Specialists in their Early Intervention program agreed that he had a speech delay and placed him in an integrated preschool. Every day he received intensive speech therapy along with occupational and physical therapy. In a short time, we were thrilled with Johnny's progress. By the end of the year, his speech delay was a non-issue. With that, the school decided he could move into a regular kindergarten classroom. Great! No further need for an IEP (Individual Education Plan.)

Along with that heartening news came the birth of my daughter, Bella, in October 2011. From the moment she was born, she used sounds and body language to express herself. But what captured the attention of everyone was how she used those special eyes of hers. Words are in them. Bella can hug and kiss you, but it's those twinkling eyes that tell you she loves you. Through them, all her thoughts: curiosity, frustration, joy, and anger – we could read like a book.

What was not as clear were Johnny's new behaviors that began springing up after pre-k. The school had told us he was "fine," so we went ahead and signed him up for the Weymouth Summer Recreation camp. Three days in, the director asked that he not come back. "Johnny was crying," counselors said, "doing his own thing, and bolting from the group." He was uncomfortable there; that much was obvious. But why?

The rest of the summer brought more bad news. Johnny began acting out at home. I wanted to believe that it was age-related, just part of growing up. But as I thought, I realized he was not socializing as he should with his peers, only us adults. I called the special ed department. "Johnny is regressing," I began, "and what he spent a year learning is dissolving in front of me. Can he join his pre-k friends in their extended school year program?" Administrators explained that their hands were tied. "Johnny was off an IEP," they said; it was not going to happen. I had to trust that we would make it through the rest of the summer, and he would improve when kindergarten began.

Meanwhile, as Bella grew, so did her personality. She was determined and strong-willed, a clone of her mother. She also had a crystal-clear understanding of who she was and who she wanted to be around. A bond with her father was forged early. It had nothing to do with me and everything to do with their shared love of roughhousing. Her eyes are starlit when she's with her dad; she is the apple of his eye.

Bella babbled as an infant, and by eighteen months she had a handful of words; "*train*" was one of them. No surprise, Johnny's first love was trains, and our house looked like a railroad yard. She could also say, "Sponge Bob," (of course) and more common words such as "Momma" and "Dada."

There were significant differences between Johnny and Bella. Johnny has a high IQ; he overcame a speech delay and became very talkative, even funny. Bella, on the other hand, showed many more signs of special needs. Yes, words came but so did worrisome behaviors. Around her first birthday, Bella began crying. Soon she was crying all day long. There were also meltdowns; Bella would flop to the ground and lie there, limp. I have never figured out what she was trying to tell us; neither has anyone else.

Bella did stop crying, but not until her second year in pre-k, probably realizing, "Okay, I get it, I am going to school." That year, her beloved teacher also made her feel safe. Feeling safe may have been *one* clue to this incessant crying, but so could her many, very real sensory issues.

Bella is both a seeker and an avoider of stimulation. She craves physical sensations such as squeezing, swinging, and jumping and avoids textures she finds too sensory – finger paints, putty, and Play-Doh. Other troubling signs began in kindergarten. Bella became aggressive and started biting on her knuckles, hurting herself. Foods for both Johnny and Bella posed other sensory issues. Anything that could not be eaten with their fingers – mashed potatoes and yogurt – was out. But fruits and meats were gobbled up.

At the age of two, Bella started in early intervention; Johnny was in pre-k. My hands were full; life was busy. Then, in January

2013, my company was outsourced, and I was laid off. The timing could not have been sweeter, allowing precious days to bond with my children. I had time to think of fun things to do while Paul, who owns our family construction business, went to work. The three of us would venture off to zoos, parks, Boston, or even to Mystic Aquarium for the day. Bella, like Johnny, enjoyed wherever we went, and since it was winter, there were minimal crowds, making it perfect. I could control situations and keep sensory flare-ups at a minimum. If either had a tantrum, they were little enough to pick up and hold or put in a stroller. I did have trouble, however, trying to figure out some of Johnny's behaviors. I wondered what was typical for a three-year-old and what could be autism; I was aware of those symptoms.

As a small family, we did well until that spring, when Johnny, Bella, and I went to the annual Boston Marathon. Bella was two, Johnny four. We stood on Boylston Street, eager to see the runners come by.

Little did we know we were standing in the wrong place, at the wrong marathon. Suddenly, we heard a blast on our right. We turned in that direction only to hear a more thunderous explosion go off even closer. Bombs, I quickly realized, were blowing up on either side of us. Thoughts came in at lightning speed, and decisions were weighing heavy. *Where should we head? Where and what is safe?* My training kicked in. I was supposed to get in and help others, but I had my children. For seconds, I was confused until I grabbed Johnny's hand, picked up Bella, abandoning her stroller, and barreled through a restaurant to their back alleyway. By now, it was pandemonium. We were swept up in the throngs of others fleeing.

I tried calling Paul to let him know we were unharmed. But with his machinery grinding away in the background, he could not hear me. As the crowds swelled, we got word that all public transportation was shutting down. We kept pace and continued to head to the water, where I knew Paul could reach us in his boat if he had to.

Thankfully, two miles later, we made one of the last ferries out of Rose Wharf. Time had warped. The boat ride to Hingham seemed endless – it all felt like hours.

Someone on Paul's construction site had tracked him down and told him the breaking news. He went cold, saying "My wife and kids are there." As much as *we* went through, Paul was dealing with this alone, in a truck, 25 miles away. I cannot imagine what went through his head.

To do this day, we are still processing it. Thousands of people were affected that day. I hear the stories. Just because someone did not get hurt there does not mean they weren't changed forever.

The three of us stayed put in our house for weeks. Paul went to work; he was our breadwinner. He saw that I was not in a good space, but he also knew I would take care of the children.

I shut down. I did not want to leave home. It was not fear that gripped me; it was survivor's remorse. I could not shake the fact that I was trained to respond to these very events and didn't. My anxiety spiraled the longer the bombers were on the loose. Days passed; I could not sleep. I was obsessing on CNN news, googling any new information, and hunting for pictures. I could not stop scrolling through the photographs I took that day.

It took a while to talk about it and even longer to gain per-spective. My grandparents, who raised me, taught me to find the positive in things. "Otherwise," they warned, "life can tear you up." I see now that the whole incident could have been worse; we could have been stuck in Boston amid the chaos.

There have been repercussions. Johnny and Bella still do not sleep in their own beds, and I continue to feel Johnny's angst when we are at any kind of gathering. But who knows, he could be feed-ing off my anxiety. And all that trickles down to Bella.

As a family, we rethought everything; we reconsidered going anywhere. For a long time, Bella could not manage the supermarket or even a peewee baseball game. It was too noisy with relentless stimulus coming at her. Johnny, even today, has trouble with sirens and other loud sounds, but at least he can speak up and ask, "What's that noise? What's going on?" To this day, we need to prepare him for everything from a fire drill at school to construction in our neighborhood. We also need to remind him that all will be all right if something unexpected happens.

We did not know how to draw the trauma out. Johnny would talk about it some but could not grasp the impact. Neither could I. All I could do was inform their schools and pull in Johnny's adjustment counselor.

That was in April. By August, Bella stopped talking. Her crying bouts also intensified, and her tantrums grew more severe. Simultaneously, Bella stopped making eye contact and lost interest in playing with her brother. She would drift off to be alone. We were losing her.

I sought help from our pediatrician, who recommended a hearing test. I was sure a hearing impairment was to blame. *I can deal with that*, I thought; *after all, I grew up around people with disabilities*. Tests showed that Bella did have hearing problems. "Fibers are damaged," the audiologist reported, "but they'll grow back."

My pediatrician could not pinpoint why Bella regressed, but Massachusetts General Hospital (MGH) could. After seven months of exhaustive testing, doctors there diagnosed her with *nonverbal autism and global cognitive delay*. Bella, we learned, was severely disabled.

She went into a program designed for young children on the spectrum, and over the next three years she made great strides. We saw her successes play out at home. Bella was paying attention longer and using pictures more often to show us what she wanted. She even began potty training; unfortunately, that training continues today.

At the age of five, Bella moved to a special ed kindergarten. On top of speech therapy, PT, and OT, Bella began ABA therapy

(Applied Behavior Analysis). I was hopeful. ABA said they could get her on a routine and manage her behaviors before they became tantrums. As for the school? I was sure they knew what Bella needed going into kindergarten. What I did not realize was that her class size was increasing. I also was not told that she would be without the one-on-one support she had for the past three years. That meant that – alone – she faced a new environment with many distractions and new expectations. Her sensory needs were on overload. Add curriculum expectations. The demands were too much for her. Bella began to regress. I knew because her behaviors spun out of control. She screamed continuously, spoke less, and barely interacted with us. I also knew Bella did not cry to create a problem; she knows what she needs but cannot get the words out. I called a meeting, brought the data, and asked the school for an out-of-district placement. "This was not going to work," I said. Weymouth agreed that her classroom did not have the resources to help her. They placed her in an 11-month program at the South Shore Collaborative's Autism Mini School in Hull. She remains there today.

Just as Bella's diagnosis came, new troubles turned up. Johnny, now five, started hitting himself and pulling at his hair. Then tantrums began. He was overwhelmed. Classmates were brand new, and he, like Bella, lost the support he needed to process it all. Nothing now was holding Johnny together.

Soon, he started bolting from the classroom. The police had to be called to search the woods for him. It became a safety issue, so the school provided a one-on-one aide. The two of them sat – all day. They did no academics; it was behavior management only. Johnny did not learn a thing. I don't know how qualified this aide was; they only needed a body to supervise him. But Johnny was in a full-blown crisis.

Things mounted at home. Since I was now back working overnights, we hired a babysitter to get Johnny off to school. She was soon grappling with bursts of him screaming and hitting. Then he refused to get on the bus. It was as if a switch was flipped. He could not say, "I'm uncomfortable." He was a kindergartener, after all.

Johnny, I decided, needed to undergo the same seven-month evaluation Bella did. I wanted to understand where these behaviors were coming from. I called MGH, scheduled the testing, and like Bella, started him in ABA. Their promise? "To increase helpful behaviors and decrease harmful ones."

Watching Johnny become a different child was the second roughest period of our life. He was so distraught; there was no consoling him. I took the next step and sought help from his school. *They would have answers*, I thought; *they were the experts after all*. Sadly, I was wrong.

I did not know how to navigate the school system at the time, but the day came when I proclaimed to the special ed director, "You will never fail my child again!" I realized right then that I did not have to pay attention to the initials at the end of his name. "*I* am the expert when it comes to my child. And if something is wrong, it's not okay that *you* aren't handling it right." (Since that declaration, I have never gotten an IEP for Johnny that I could accept on the first round.)

I didn't know about "coping strategies" for children; I didn't know about CBT (Cognitive Behavioral Therapy), ABA therapy, or BCBA (Board Certified Behavior Analyst.) Nobody handed me a special ed dictionary saying, "This is what you need." Unfortunately, you figure it out when you are at your worst – in a crisis.

Battling for his services stretched on while Johnny persevered through the strenuous testing at MGH. Finally, doctors diagnosed him with autism and ADHD (Attention Deficit Hyperactivity Disorder.) That was March 2015, a year after Bella's finding.

Johnny's diagnosis was more upsetting than Bella's. Her

speech regression was a warning that this was going to go backward before going forward. So, we were eager to move ahead with whatever we needed to do. But Johnny? Autistic? The diagnosis came as a shock. My husband, the papa bear, had an even harder time; that's *his* boy!

How could they have said he was fine? I will always wonder where he would be today had he gotten the support he needed in kindergarten. I will never know, but I do know that he would have been spared the trauma.

Given this diagnosis, the school put Johnny on an IEP (Individual Education Plan.) But discussion about his placement took months. The town finally met my request. Johnny would go full-time to a substantially separate elementary school program. However, he had to remain in the classroom that overwhelmed him; his IEP would not go into effect until September.

Johnny did well transitioning to his new school. He was on an intense IEP designed to pull his academics back up to grade level. He did not have a one-on-one aide, but he had teachers who understood him, old friends by his side, and a familiar normalcy. I imagine he said to himself, "This is what I need to get me where I need to go." Johnny had a great year!

Technically, Johnny is now in fourth grade. His academics are strong despite some weakness in math which, with help, is at grade level. He reads well (and a lot) and is even in some general ed classes. He is incredibly articulate, and his descriptions are delightfully detailed. His vocabulary is astonishing. One would never know he was once diagnosed with a speech delay.

Johnny amuses us. He likes to talk about adult subjects; one is politics. His words are ones you and I would choose; they are not those of a ten-year-old. He doesn't discuss the issues because he has already formed opinions. I call him, "Our future mayor."

His storytelling is also fascinating. He has a phenomenal imagination and can make up a story on the spot. Johnny also creates original and elaborate audio scripts all the time. If he is playing with his plushie toys, you might hear a tale that goes on for a few minutes or one that spans the entire day. Even if he takes a break, he will go right back to it.

When it comes to things he likes, his recall is astonishing. He developed an affinity for model trains as a baby, entranced by their moving parts. Anything he has heard or read about them he remembers.

Johnny also likes all sorts of movies. Certain characters captivate him, so he draws them. Our routine these days is to watch a Scooby-Doo or Marvel movie before bedtime. I cannot randomly pick one out – he must watch them in order, no jumping around.

It is those social skills that elude Johnny; he cannot read cues. He does not understand, for example, that when someone is upset, it is probably not the time to talk to them. And if Johnny sees someone struggling at school, he feels he should get involved. "The teacher is mean," he will report to me, not realizing that she is already helping.

Typically, Johnny does not initiate a conversation; he watches, though. He also cannot converse but will play with someone who has similar interests: trains and Thomas the Tank, Five Nights at Freddie's, and, of course, Marvel movies and characters. This year, Johnny has taken a liking to a fifth-grader who he recognizes is equally mature and on his wavelength academically. Not long ago, they went off to the movies together – his first outing without me.

Johnny has been in the same program for several years. It has moved to other buildings, and at one point, his class went through three teachers in two years. That meant more transitions for him, more preparation for me. Then COVID-19 hit.

Everything last March tipped upside down. I jumped in. First thought? A schedule! After creating that, I set up a classroom in our dining room. I knew these two mainstays needed to be in place before breakfast, even if he were to return to the building in a week. Bella, too, was home. So, with Bella on one side and Johnny on the other, I became their one-on-one aide, following along with them on Zoom or Google Meet.

That worked through the summer, even though remote learning was insufferable for them both. Zoom is exhausting with seven students, on seven levels, learning seven different ways. Johnny loved seeing his classmates, but his attention would turn to a friend having a meltdown or someone else taking the teacher's time. Soon, he was overtaxed, and the fiddling with his ear or his fingers would begin. His frustration would mount; I knew I had to intervene. "Go outside and swing," I suggested, or "Put on *Go Noodle* and dance!" On cold, snowy days, he would hop on our living room swing and pump until his feet touched the ceiling. Daily, I promised that if he got through the day, he could do art or a project with me. We never took a day off; we might have escaped on a mental health day here and there, but we did not let up on the academics.

Bella's Collaborative was remarkable. When her school shut down during the pandemic, they had her online with others in no time. They mailed activities to do and videos for her to watch. Teachers also dropped off materials daily – including instructions for OT and PT. Doing physical therapy at home had its challenges. I never knew if I was positioning her correctly or if she was even benefiting. But we kept at it!

And we kept up with ABA. That therapy can be long and intense on any week. But during COVID-19, ABA was ratcheted up. Johnny and Bella had daily sessions lasting multiple hours. Johnny continues to work on flexibility, namely adopting strategies such as wall pushups, deep breathing, even jumping jacks to help manage when things don't go his way. It's a process, but he has mastered knowing when to say, "I need a break" before becoming overly frustrated.

There are so many goals to stay on top of, especially with

Applied Behavior Analysis

Bella. She works on attending to a task, sitting at a table for longer and longer periods, and using "Touch Chat" on her AAC (augmentative assistive communication) device effectively. Bella still has tantrums, so therapists watch for the behaviors that precede them, then redirect her. We also help her avoid biting herself by replacing that sensory need with something else. Right now, it's a *Chewy Q* – a therapeutic toy she can gnaw on.

Bella's sensory issues are so severe. They get in the way of her independence and self-care. She struggles, for example, with having her hair combed and her teeth brushed. A tag in a t-shirt can impact the entire day. Lately, she has been obsessive/compulsive about her finger and toenails. I know because she continuously bites at them. The sensation of a hangnail can overwhelm her and become the focus for the day.

Bella has her concerns – then there are mine. I have no way of knowing if she is crying because of a sensory issue or because she is not feeling well. She cannot tell me if she has a sore throat, and just taking her temperature is difficult. Bella has a history of pneumonia. I learned that the hard way when her lung collapsed the first time. This worry was amplified during the pandemic.

Homeschooling is not a job for me, but we did it! They did it! Johnny went back to school in September, Bella much earlier. I did enjoy our time but must admit there were days when I wanted to pull my hair out. I did not know if I could go on. Before COVID-19, I had gone back to work full-time from home. During COVID-19, we went to school from 8:00 to 3:00, and then I began my workday at 3:30 when Johnny's ABA therapist came. My day ended at midnight.

For the moment, the waters are calm. I can reflect a bit and see we have "Across the Spectrum" right here. It is all-encompassing.

I remember when Bella became nonverbal and withdrawn, Johnny did not react right away. Soon enough, his questions came. "Why doesn't Bella talk? Why doesn't Bella play with me?" I explained that it's not because she doesn't like you, she loves you!

"She wants you to talk to her," I continued, "but she thinks a little differently and needs her space sometimes."

There were other times when Johnny, in a meltdown, would say, "I don't understand why Bella has to pinch me?" I explained to him, "It's her way of getting your attention; she can't say, 'Johnny, I need you.'" I had to repeat this explanation frequently before Johnny could process it.

Bella is resourceful and self-reliant, always doing her own thing. She does not play, per se, but enjoys holding her favorite things – the "Little People," SpongeBob, or musical books. Bella loves music! We have several Bluetooth speakers around; she controls the volume and the music on all of them from her iPad or my iPhone.

Bella gives Johnny a run for his money. If he has the iPad, she will grab it, or if he is eating something she wants, she will help herself. But over the last year, I have seen a change in her towards him. When Johnny could break away from his Zoom classes, he would lean over to help her do her lesson. She noticed. One of the best things about COVID-19 was watching them bond – all those hours sitting next to each other paid off.

There are days when she will seek him out just to make sure he is still around. But there are other days when she isolates and does not want to be near him. She makes that clear to Johnny and others. You will quickly know if she enjoys having you around because Bella can sense people the minute she meets them. And it's those eyes again that will tell you it's okay to stay there. We once hired a babysitter to get the two off the school bus. It ended poorly; I had to tell her that it was not going to work. That is how it goes in our house. If my children do not warm up to you, I will not attempt to fix it.

Bella has a great sense of humor. She loves men, and she loves attention. Bella also knows just how to tickle certain funny bones. People look at me like I am crazy when I tell them what a comic she is. "But she doesn't speak!?" they query.

Johnny's humor also delights us. He is an old soul, full of hilarious old-fashioned expressions. "I'm gonna hit the hay" is one. He also dazzles us with words he chooses; instead of "yes," he pops out with, "Sure thing." He's funny even in general conversation. The other day, he told me a story and asked which character I liked best. When I said that I wasn't sure, he responded, "Well, here are some suggestions."

Given their humor and their accomplishments, we have considerable joy in our life. But we know there will be struggles ahead. I can predict a few. Because Johnny is so articulate, it can sometimes appear that he does not need special ed supports. But he does. And, as hard as it is to keep standing up, I will be there every step of the way to ensure he has them.

The town has changed Johnny's program a lot, and for a child with transition issues, that's not the best. He has met his challenges of new buildings and new teachers with remarkable resilience. He has also grown up with Bella's severe disabilities. Today he completely understands and loves her unconditionally. I don't think he would have grown into such a delightful young person had he not experienced all that he did.

Johnny will accomplish whatever he sets his mind to. It might be through smaller steps taken slower, but he will persevere. Paul sees Johnny driving one of his trucks in the future. I see him becoming an advocate not only for himself, but for others like Bella. There is an interest there. Over the past few months, Johnny has read a lot about Dr. Temple Grandin, the international lecturer on autism. Then, in a fourth-grade presentation, he *introduced* her to his classmates. No matter what he chooses to do, he will put his heart and soul into it.

Johnny knows that during the worst of our worst, I was there. He has seen me upset and heard my concern talking to his teachers, but he knows I am doing all this for him. And it is through him watching that he has come to understand that no matter what, you do not give up; you keep moving forward – a lesson I learned from my grandmother.

And Bella? We have nothing but hope! After an incredible start, she has mastered some important (nonverbal) communication. Last week she came home, took out her iPad, and requested a paintbrush and paint. I smiled; it was the first time she has initiated anything like that. She is also becoming more self-sufficient. She can reach into the refrigerator and grab a juice box or scale any counter to find cookies. You can also be sure Bella will locate that iPad of hers! Once on any electronic device, she will navigate her way around to get to YouTube and find SpongeBob.

None of our goals involves bringing Bella's speech back. We focus on her happiness. That means stepping into her world. If she is happy being silent, that is all right with us. Most likely, ABA methodology will be a constant throughout her lifetime. Without it, Bella would not have been able to sit down and do a three-minute task a couple of years ago. Nor would she have *ever* given up her iPad. That and more has changed. She can now understand what we expect of her, and she complies. Today, she can withstand going to the grocery store, the mall, and even Johnny's street hockey games. Her crowning achievement? Bella, still sensitive to noise, people, and overstimulation, walked down the aisle of a cousin's wedding. She surprises us.

These are our victories. And for many, it is hard to understand the complexities of our life. People call asking," Do you want to go out tonight?" Raising two children on the spectrum amounts to a second full-time job, both done on very little sleep. Nothing is as simple as calling a babysitter. It is not only the daily school issues we have to address, but home concerns as well. Add in the hours of ABA therapists in my house every day, endless doctor visits, and the daily unknowns. When I tell people that I cannot do something in the morning because I have a school meeting at 1:00, it's because I need to prepare. I am not going there to hear about Johnny's A in

Reading. I am going to examine every aspect of their lives and pave the way for their future.

Paul and I are committed to our children and work well as a team. He is a great dad. The minute that door opens at night, they both run to play with him. He does not put the demands on them that I do. They seek him out for love and nurturing; they know to come to me when something needs figuring out. Paul also supports me. When I go to him saying, "We have an issue here," he listens and shares his thoughts but then defers back to me. He remembers my background and my training and realizes that I know what I am doing.

There are times when I wonder why this is the life we live. There has to be a greater purpose. I often think it is because maybe our story will help someone else.

Author's Note

This book relies on each mother's personal experience and memories. Some details remain unknown or forgotten, and some things have changed since the writing of this. I have not embellished or invented anything. However, I did change a few names and locations to protect the privacy of individuals and institutions. These are their stories as told to me, written in their voice.

Acknowledgements

So much gratitude; too few adequate words.

To each of the mothers: Millie, Dawn, Jackie, Janine, Betsy, and Danielle. The world is a better place, thanks to you. Each of you stepped forward to introduce us to what it means to live with an autistic child. You braved sharing your stories with me; thank you for trusting me to write them.

And to Judy Scott, MD, who was to be part of this book, but COVID-19 brought her to the front lines. *Our* deep appreciation for your selfless work. *My* many thanks for writing our book's introduction.

To my husband, John. It is because of you that this book is in others' hands. Thank you for your steadfast patience and abundant love, especially these last three years. You have always been my true North.

To my brother, Carlton Tucker, who, with great care, read endless iterations over these years and remained willing to take my calls for one more detail! The gloves are off – no more *"discussions."* **We** did it! Here is where a word of thanks does not measure up to the depth of gratitude.

To my sister, Mary Evelyn Tucker, whose keen insight improved the story each time I asked and whose timely calls always placed me back on terra firma. Your heartening words and abiding love were/are invaluable!

To my other brothers and sister: Duane, Paul, Libby, and Peter. I wouldn't be where I am without you.

And to the many helpers along the way. Some who read, suggested, or answered questions, and others who kept me propped up: Thank you, Beth Moran, Cindy Wordell, Edie Coletti, Ellen

Green, Emily Uhl, Georgenne Foley, Janet Cann, Janine Birmingham, Jody Dougherty, John Henderson, Judy and Jay Carter, Kathy Staska, Liz Souffrant, Mary Dollar, Michael Rogers, Michelle Gregory, Pam Rudolph, Stu Withrow, and Victor Wang.

Add the painstaking work of Omni Publishing's editor, Theresa Driscoll, the photography and layout work of David Heath and Dave Derby who put it all in a cover alive with color.

To my constellation of friends for enduring my endless talks about "the book" and loving me at my best and my worst. Thank you, Annabelle Wallace, Annie Stevens, Arya Francesca Jenkins, Barbara Heyde, Barbara Umbrianna, Cindy Blish, Connie Coutts, Dorraine Porter, Eilene Davidson, Jackie Leach, Jeannie Hogan, Judy Cully, Karen Sheerin, Kelly Meader, Marj Bates, Maryanne Leonard, "M" Wright, and Virginia Mills.

I am also grateful for the "Bright Spots" and those at Seaside for keeping me on a steady path.

I cannot end this page without mentioning Henry M. Quinlan. His steely guidance and brilliant clarity have taught me so much. Henry is an exceptionally skilled publisher and agent, an even quicker and smarter editor, and an all-around extraordinary human being. I smile when I think of the coincidence that brought us together. My life has become enriched because of you. Thank you.

About the Author

Anne Tucker Roberts is an innovative teacher and writer of memoirs. For nearly two decades, she taught adolescents with intellectual and developmental disabilities. She was recognized as a Master Teacher and received a "Golden Apple" for professional excellence.

In 2018, she published, *Five Courageous Mothers,* the remarkable stories of mothers of her students, who raised children with Down syndrome in the years before there were services. This, her second book, is the result of collaborative work between Anne and mothers who raised children with autism.

A graduate of Boston College, Anne later earned a combined Master's degree in Education and Special Education. She continues her work as a guardian for people with developmental disabilities and lives in Scituate, MA, with John, her husband of 35 years.

Praise for Across the Spectrum:
Mothers of Autistic Children Speak!

"My husband and I were both fully absorbed in this book – so much so that having put my laundry into the wash at 9:00 am it was still sitting there at 7:00 pm."
-Judy and Jay Carter, Dedham, MA

"Across the Spectrum brims with practical information and key truths for success in a life with autism."
-Judith Scott, M. D., Mother of Jeffrey, Age 21

"An excellent resource for young families dealing with a newly diagnosed child. *Across the Spectrum* provides a unique behind the scenes view of families raising children with ASD. Stories are written from the heart and include the heartaches of what might have been. The challenges of getting the correct diagnosis and much needed services are very real. The triumphs and successes of individuals with ASD and the acceptance by their families and communities are also very real."
-Mary Burt, Executive Director
South Shore Support Services, Weymouth, MA

"Anne Tucker Roberts' *Across the Spectrum: Mothers of Autistic Children Speak!* is a powerful book that will empower educators to understand the experiences of raising a child with autism. It gives invaluable insight and appreciation to navigate working with families and being able to collaborate with compassion and understanding of the child and their family."
-Maureen M. Gattine, MS, BCBA, LABA
Mini School Program Director
South Shore Educational Collaborative, Hingham, MA

"Anne Tucker Roberts has done it again! Bringing us on a ride through the stories of six families trying to find a path for their children with autism, many in the days when Autism wasn't as well known or supported as it is today. They are stories of struggle, tenacity and love, as well as triumph!"
Chris White, Ed. D. President/CEO
Road To Responsibility, Inc, Marshfield, MA

"My heart is very full after just reading these authentic and impactful stories told by mothers. They chronicle their own experiences and growth loving and parenting a child with autism through the various ages and stages. There is wisdom for the pain but also triumph and celebration for the journey with its own unique joy along the way."
-Deborah Donovan, Principal
Boston Higashi School, Randolph, MA

"Every chapter was compelling. The stories of these families brought tears to my eyes, a lump in my throat, and an ache in my heart - all punctuated by lightness and joy. I marvel at the courage and unconditional love of these parents. They are an inspiration, and I am so pleased that this book brings their voices to light. Just as like-minded parents started the disability rights movement back in the 1950s, the voices of these parents are keenly needed today!"
-Daryl Ann Cook-Ivan, MSW, Executive Director
The Arc of the South Shore

"As I read these stories, I am once again reminded of the individuality of the people we support who are diagnosed with ASD and the deep love and resolve of their incredible families! This book should be read by all families who love and care for someone with ASD and by all professionals who are fortunate to work these amazing people!"
-Beth Moran Liuzzo, Area Director, Brockton Area Office,
MA Department of Developmental Services

"These honest and insightful portrayals of the lives of mothers of neurodiverse children will resonate with many parents and offer guidance and hope."
-Ron Suskind, Author of "Life Animated: A Story of Sidekicks, Heroes, and Autism."